Farmer's Diary

Charlie Allan

Illustrations by
Turnbull

Ardo Publishing Company
Buchan

I am grateful to the *Glasgow Herald* for permission to reproduce these articles, which first appeared in print in that newspaper.

C.A.

Published by Ardo Publishing Company, Buchan
Printed by Famedram Publishers Ltd, Aberdeenshire

Foreword

This volume represents something close to the achievement of a life's ambition. For the diary is in fact a column which I have submitted weekly to the readers of the *Glasgow Herald* since the autumn of 1989.

I might have been writing for them far sooner though, for from the days before my teens it was always my earnest intention to follow my father's footsteps and join the staff of the *Glasgow Herald* as soon as might be. As graduation approached a salary of £600 per annum was even mentioned.

In the event, the glitter of gold diverted me from my chosen path and I got a job in Glasgow University, at no fewer than than £800 a year. It was sad not to be joining the *Herald* but a married man had to think of his responsibilities.

So you see, when, almost thirty years later, Ian Morrison asked me if I would become a regular contributor to the *Herald* it was not surprising that I almost took his arm off at the elbow. It was partly that my ropey farming needed a bit of diversifying but it was much more than that. It was a chance to fulfil, in part at least, what I had, for much of my life, regarded as my fate. I am grateful to him for the chance.

The idea that this might make a book came from readers of the *Herald* and when the second letter flooded in I decided to go for it. I don't think I should thank them until I see whether or not I lose my shirt on the deal.

But I do want to thank Jim Turnbull for letting me use his cartoons, which will provide relief for those bored by the text. I'm also indebted to Maris and Beverly who helped dig the cartoons Jim had lost out of the *Glasgow Herald* library and for help with my spelling from Maggie Williams and Apple Mac™. Eleanor Stewart and Bill Williams made special sacrifices to get this up to schedule and I will try not to forget that.

But mostly I want to thank you for buying this book... or even for borrowing it.

Dedication and disclaimer

The diary is dedicated to the boys in the New Deer and Methlick Agricultural Discussion Group.
Any resemblance to any member of which, though at times uncanny, is purely incidental and will be denied in court.

CHARLIE ALLAN was born in 1939 in a taxi going over Stirling Bridge from Blairlogie to the hospital in Stirling. When his parents were away taking care of Mr. Hitler he moved to Aberdeenshire to his grandparents' farm of North Ythsie near Tarves. He liked that so much that after the war he moved his parents to nearby Little Ardo, which had been his grandmother's family farm.

Educated at Dartingtonhall School and Aberdeen University, he spent most of his time playing rugby, cricket and basketball to university standard and junior football, as well as winning the all-round athletics championship at the Aboyne Highland Games and the World Cabar Tossing Championship. He holds the doubtful honour of having lost that, in Australia, to an Englishman.

A degree in Economics led to an extended period of leisure in the Universities of Glasgow, St. Andrews and Strathclyde, where he published an exciting book on taxation and retired a senior lecturer in 1973 to develop the farming interests he had started in 1969.

That meant a move to the family farm and a long period of financial decline as new sheds were put up and stock numbers increased. Farming proved so easy that the author combined that with a five year spell as Radio Scotland's Farming Producer, writing and recording Bothy Ballads and writing short stories, a volume of which has been coming out shortly for the last six years.

His wife Fiona rescued him from that for the life of a gentleman in Kenya while she worked a computer for the government for three years.

As this Diary starts the family have just returned to Little Ardo.

Fiona and he are still married with four flown children and three grandchildren.

Much has to be done if I am to be remembered as an improver

I AM a farmer who is starting again from scratch having returned recently to the family farm after three years in Kenya.

My wife was installing computer systems for the Kenyan government and I went along to be nothing more strenuous than Fiona's best friend.

People who knew me in Scotland said a life of ease would drive me mad, but I found I was, in fact, ideally suited to it.

Mind you, I did have my responsibilities – I had to start the cook/housekeeper and the gardener each morning, and the boys at the club expected me to be in the library by 11 o'clock.

We were in Nairobi which, despite being on the equator, is never too hot as it is over 5000 feet above sea level. We had all the facilities of an international city – around sixty first class restaurants with beer at 30p a pint and fillet steak at 80p a pound in the shops.

The gardener and the cook thought themselves well paid at £14 a week for the pair.

So why did we return to the plain stanes of Aberdeenshire? That's a question I often ask myself as I run round the farm like the Little Dutch Boy trying desperately to plug all the leaks in my emerging agricultural system.

But it's a rhetorical question, for I have rehearsed the answer well.

It certainly wasn't that we were fed up with the warm sun on our backs, but that we didn't want to become grumpy like so many Europeans we met in Kenya.

7

HE'S YOUR NEW
MAN ,,,,AN' ME
AH'M THE AULD
DUG'S COUSIN.

KENYA

TRADITION

For some reason they live in fear of a return home, while moaning all the time about the poor food on Kenya Railways and everything that a fading memory tells them was so much better in the old country.

And, with old age beckoning, we didn't want to do as my parents had done and land so far away from our family that there was no-one to bring in the coal for us and fight with tradesmen.

But if that had been all, we'd have stayed in Africa.

Fiona had made the decision to have a few years away from the snell winds of the North East, I sold the stock, had a roup of everything that might be stolen or broken when we were away, and gave up my job with the BBC. But the deal was that I would decide when we would come home.

What motivated the decision that three years in Africa was enough was the peasant's instinct for his land.

My great-great-grandfather came to this farm in the middle of the last century. He had won an award from the Royal Highland and Agricultural Society for drainage work on his farm in the next parish, and the laird had rewarded him with a huge rent increase. William Yull moved to Little Ardo rather than pay the laird for the fruits of his own labour.

My maternal grandfather, Maitland Mackie, a former

president of the National Farmer's Union of Scotland, had bought the place from the Earls of Aberdeen in 1920, my parents had bought it in 1945 and I, in turn, had bought it from them in 1976.

I am the only child, so it has fallen on me to carry on this family farm until another generation is ready for it. There are 250 acres of good second class land, buildings that are little more than than woodworm holes held together by tradition, and we have the hill cow subsidy on 100 acres.

There is much to be done if I'm to be remembered as an improver – and I could hardly have done that from Africa.

Harvest always seems to create that atmosphere of hysteria

What is this world if full of care,
We have no time to stand and stare?

AS I'VE scurried about my business of harvesting in recent weeks, I have found it hard to get that couplet of William Hunter Davies's out of my head.

I'm a one man band and that means seeing to the livestock and then trying to keep the grain drier full, the combine empty and the lorries turned round with the minimum delay. I'm not complaining of course, but there was an awful lot of grain this year. We had just under 28 cwts of rape seed, three and a half tonnes of winter barley, and over two tonnes of spring barley. I don't like too much guesswork so I can't tell you what the wheat is yet but it is over three tonnes.

I might have managed the harvesting bit all right but what I had forgotten when I was planning to farm again in Scotland is that you have to do most of the spring work at the same time. The fields have to be cleared and half of next year's crop sown before harvest is finished.

Quite my worst moment this week was when I returned from assisting at a stiff calving to discover that the contractor who was sowing had overtaken me and his manure and seed cart was empty. He had decided to help himself but had stuck himself in the ploughing while helping himself to the wrong manure.

I needed the digger because a lorry had arrived unannounced for a load of wheat and another lorry had arrived with eleven tonnes of seed wheat. Thank goodness the combine had finished by that time.

A few days earlier I had had quite a turn when we were combining our farthest away field. I had been at it since six, it was now four o'clock in the afternoon and I still hadn't had my lunch. I was struggling to keep the combine going as I had about a mile to run and it was not a smooth road. Despite that and terrified that the stuff would heat, between loads I quickly sneaked on a batch to dry.

I jumped aboard and was tearing along the back road to the field when I met a similar old International with a blue cart, just like mine. For just a moment I was filled with relief. It was all right. I hadn't stopped the combine. Sanity returned quickly of course and I soon realised that, fast as I was, I hadn't met myself on the way back – but it does show you the sort of hysteria you can get into at harvest time.

Yes, my harvest is a far cry from those my father enjoyed between his demobilisation in 1945 and his retirement in the early seventies. He tried working in his first harvest but was found by the grieve to be "Nae use ava'". That suited the old man just fine and from that day onwards his harvesting was done mostly with one foot on the second bar of the gate and with the pipe in his mouth.

No doubt a creative writer like John R. Allan was doing more than just standing and staring. Certainly he did a good deal of listening. He claims to have benefited from the following interchange between myself, aged 16, and the grieve who had been so unkind about his own ability in the harvest field.

We were stooking and had stopped at the end of a row so that the grieve could fill his pipe. The teenager was heard to say, "Aye grieve, this stookin's makin me real tired ye ken."

"Is that so," a long suffering voice replied. "Well I'm tired tae, but it's nae the stookin that's makin me tired, it's listenin tae your news."

Whether the story is true matters not, but the scene does illustrate the changing pace of life on the small farm. While my father was keeping the gate in place he had six men doing the brute work of harvest and yielding unto him a modest profit year on year.

Happy the man whose wish and care,
A few paternal acres bound,
Content to breath his native air,
On his own ground.

Buchan's party won't be ruined by coming changes in the weather

WELL THAT'S it. Harvest is finished – and finished with honour. We had 3.6 tonnes of wheat to add to the 3.5 tonnes of winter barley, 2.5 tonnes of spring barley and 1.4 tonnes of oilseed rape. Not perhaps our best ever but when you think that the drying charges have been very low it really has been a great harvest here in Buchan.

Indeed many people have done much better than me – at least if you believe what they say in the pub. I have one neighbour who struggled with his conscience all week before deciding that it wasn't worth being a liar for two tonnes of wheat. If only he had had two tonnes more he would have averaged four tonnes to the acre. Almost 80 cwts against an average in England of 56 cwt.

We've had a desperate few years here and we're fairly enjoying the change in fortune, the upsurge of optimism is remarkable. At a roup last Saturday, prices went through the roof. Good tractors were up 20% on three months ago and cattle feed rings (with only a little rust and no more than one bar missing) were making 112% of the new price.

My neighbour, Mossie, who averaged 1.8 tonnes of rape seed and had the double bounty of 180 sows in this time of booming bacon sales, has coined a new three year rotation – winter barley, oilseed rape and Bermuda.

Of course we do understand deep down that our current good fortune only repairs one year of former damage and that the weather, having changed, is likely to change again.

But we're not going to let that spoil the party.

My seventy acres of wheat produced a shining yellow cascade. We decided to dump it in one of the covered pits made redundant by the success of bagged silage. But that was soon full and so was the second one, and the old barn, until we were couping it all over the farmyard and wheat ran out of every door.

When the combine finally left I was alone in the sunshine. There was warmth about. For a short while there seemed to be no hurry, and the 'pressure' people go on about nowadays had lifted.

I flopped down on the grain dunes and savoured a rare moment of fulfilment.

On our way home from Africa we had passed over the Sahara. The mountains of sand stretched on and on. As I opened my eyes the heaps of yellow corn were the sands of the desert. I saw myself a latter-day T.E. Lawrence in the more glorious parts of his saga.

Yes my 260 tonnes, all seventy cart-loads of it, though perhaps a little less in extent was just like the waving dunes of the Sahara.

As I lay there in the lee of one of the cart-loads I remembered the two soldiers in the second world war who had somehow got lost during Montgomery's travails in North Africa.

They wandered round and round while the rations and the

water dwindled. At last they sat down behind an enormous bank of sand to face death with the comfort of their last cigarette.

They were reminiscing about home and the good times when the one asked of the other, "What day would it be anyway, Willie?"

"Wednesday the fourth of August, Andra."

"First Wednesday in August? Man, man, Turra Show day," said Andrew wistfully. He looked up at the blazing desert sun. "Mind you Willie, they're gettin' a grand day for the show."

October 23, 1989

Shocks all the way with each visit to the sale ring

THE HARVEST over, I've been turning my attention to the livestock and there, I have to say, the news is not all good. When I returned from Africa in April there were no livestock on the place bar some rats and two cats, but we soon put that right. We put down poison for the rats and killed the cats.

The second move was to get back the four Simmentals that had failed to make it to our sale before we left for Kenya. They had calves at foot so immediately we were up to eight head.

Impressive as that was, with seventy acres of grass to be stocked, I felt I needed more – so off I went to the store sales to get myself some grazers.

There is no way I can describe the shock I got. It seems like no time at all since I went to Oban in the spring and bought bullocks that were growthless but beefy, for £80 and finished them off the grass. But now I

was being asked £600 for the sort of cattle I wanted to buy.

I went to three markets before I got a bid and it was at the fourth that I made my first purchase. He was the plainest Ayrshire I've ever seen – except for the steer he's turned into. He weighed 8 cwts and cost £350.

I tell you it has been awful looking at that beast all summer and what a job to keep him away from the roadsides where all my neighbours could see him. He has put on weight mind, or at least height. Every time I see the brute I think about the rich man getting to heaven and the camel getting through the eye of a needle. This one certainly looks like a camel and I think maybe there is hope for the rich man yet for my stot could just about get through the eye of a needle so thin is he.

And to think that I bought him to get the new beef special

16

premium of £29 a head. I was told I could get 90 such payments up to Christmas but the way Lanky is going I'll still be stuffing barley into him this time next year.

My purchases did improve but by mid-May I was looking for a tenant for 30 acres of grass. That brought in £1,500 which was most welcome as I just treat them as pleasant bonuses when they arrive.

At any rate the beef special premia were not the only subsidies I took into account in deciding what livestock to buy. You see, a hundred acres of Little Ardo has recently become eligible for the Hill Cow subsidy. I worked it out that with luck the subsidy would

A BACK LIKE THE ROOF OF A HOUSE!

HIS LEGS KEEP GROWIN'

16 cwts.

HANDY IN THIS WEATHER!

Turnbull.

would have nothing to sell until harvest time.

Now wise men do say that you should never do anything on the farm just because there are subsidies available. Of course you shouldn't do daft things just to get subsidies but you can hardly ignore them – pay the bought-in costs of keeping the cow and her calf. It would be like having the calves to sell each year at no expense to me. So I set off to have me 40 breeding cows.

Well now, if I got a surprise in the store ring, how do you think I felt trying to buy 40

Hereford Friesian cows with calves at foot? I'd have got change out of £40,000 but not much. So it was back to the drawing board.

The North College are well on with a scheme to put embryos from beef cattle, fertilised by a beef bull, into your cows so that you can produce pure beef cattle from your dairy cows. From the point of view of calf production there is no need for a great big Hereford-Friesian cow because the calf gets none of its genes from your cow. The best cow would therefore be one with a womb and udder and little else – especially price.

Logic pointed clearly to the Jersey breed and I am set to buy me a herd of them. But when I told my cousin Maitland Mackie that I was to buy 40 Jerseys he said that was a capital idea. "Forget about farming and buy Jerseys. At least they'll keep you warm."

The advice was sound no doubt but I'm off the the Channel Islands in the morning, cheque book in hand. I'll tell you how I got on next week.

To Jersey cheque book in hand

I PROMISED to tell you this week about my quest for the ideal beef cow. I had decided that, in this day of transplant breeding, the logical cow was the Jersey. She wouldn't eat much, she would calve easily and she would give her calves the creamiest milk and plenty of it.

The first snag was that although Jersey cattle are very cheap in Aberdeenshire there weren't any to be had. I contacted my old friend, the auctioneer John Thornborrow and he was able to get some from the North of England. I started my beef herd with two old dears who had been on their way to the slaughterhouse... they cost two hundred each... and five heifers which looked not bad at two hundred and

AYE, JERSEYS ARE RIGHT DAINTY EATERS!

fifty. The heifers were guaranteed free of the bull so only two of them were in calf and of course the cows had been free of the bull for a year or two.

Promising as that start may have been, I determined to step up the pace of expansion. I would go to Jersey itself.

If you are cynical you will no doubt be shaking your head knowingly and thinking that I just went for a cheap holiday on the firm but it was not so. I went to a dispersal of one of the old established herds on the island.

Attending that sale was like spending the day in another, gentler world. The machinery was quite literally scrap and sold for far below our scrap prices. The farm buildings were small and inconvenient.

But the sun shone and everybody seemed to know everybody else but me and there was a leisurely 'Sunday' feel about.

We sat in a circle of bales in a field overlooking the bay at St. Helier. The company would be about fifty souls. The cows were looking a picture… all haltered and tied to a rail. I was to find out later that their beautifully turned horns can be grabbed in the field to allow worming and the like.

There isn't enough work on Jersey to justify a full-time auctioneer so one of the farmers does it. I was warned that I would have to give a good wave to attract his attention and so it proved. To get my first bid in I had to stand up, throw my catalogue in the air and finally shout.

Not that it made much difference what the bidders did. The first lot was withdrawn at 320 guineas and the second at 380. The fifth lot did sell for 520 guineas but that was well beyond my budget. Like many others there I gave up bidding till after the sale. Then I let everyone else have a go and finally bought the remains.

Now you may well think that it would be a dear business getting my treasures home from the Channel Islands but you'd be wrong. The Jersey government subsidises the export of cows to the tune of a hundred pounds a head. That gets them to Poole free and I was able to get them home from there for fifteen pounds a head. So now my beef herd was up to seventeen and still below three hundred pounds a piece.

In fact I managed to get another fifteen at a dispersal sale in Somerset. They all arrived home, together with thirty of the dearest calves I've

20

ever heard of far less bought. The idea was that the calves would suckle the cows.

Unfortunately that scheme went down better with the calves than with the cows and, what with there being too few of them in full milk and the shortage of grass that the drought has produced, it has been a poorish success

I will of course have to wait some time before I know if the whole idea was a disaster or only just a mistake. Much will depend on how the transplanted calves turn out next year and how well the Simmental bull we have been using will nick with the Jerseys.

In the meantime, as I look at those cross calves which cost £290 a head five months ago, I am not sure I could get the buying bill back if I were to put them on the market.

On the credit side the Jerseys have been easy to feed... twelve heifers have become fat on three acres of natural grass... and they are bonny beasts to view from the bedroom window.

Ae last drink frae the well

THIS WEEK'S been dominated by the troubles I've been having with my water. Not only has there not been enough on the place to feed the cattle but we've had to take action to stop poisoning ourselves.

This comes as a great shock to me as I have always believed that Little Ardo had not only the best water in the world but an unlimited supply of it.

When we were children we used to drink huge draughts of the stuff out of an old enamelled mug that for years lay beside the well. I once drank ten mugs full after a game of football and would have had more had my little stomach not been full to the pain, and when I was in foreign fields recently one of the little things I used to yearn for was a drink from that well.

At the turn of the century

AE LAST DRINK FRAE THE WELL!

OCH, NO ANOTHER!

IT KEEPS THEM GOING!

Turnbull

my great grandfather sent his daughters by turns to get him "ae last drink" from that well. Unfortunately for the daughters, his love of that water was better than his judgment of how long he would live. It went on for weeks until the two girls were heartily sick of trekking outside for yet another last drink.

Eventually, the legitimate one announced that she wasn't going again to the well. The old man would know no difference if they took the rest of his last drinks from the tap in the kitchen. But in Dickensian style, the illegitimate daughter insisted that after all the old man had done for them the least they could do was to get him a last drink from the well of his choice, however uncertain the timing.

Well now, with all the stories of polluted water supplies we decided, on our return from Africa, to have the water at Little Ardo analysed. And that proved the old man right to cherish the water from the well. The stuff in the house had some thirty times the safe dose of lead in it as well as nitrates which were said to be too strong to be safe for suckling babies.

So this week we have dug up and replaced all the old piping and, though suckling isn't as common here as it used to be, installed a filter for nitrates in the kitchen.

But salutary as that experience was it wasn't as shocking as finding that our water supply, as well as being unsafe for human consumption, wasn't sufficient to the needs of the farm. What brought that to a head was our test for TB and for brucellosis. That entailed assembling all the cattle from the various outposts of the farm and putting them for the three days of the test on the home water supply.

Now my grandfather gave as one of his excuses for buying the farm in 1920 (at no less a figure than £4250) the fact that the farm would 'neither droot nor droon'. Sloping as it does down to the Ythan Valley it will surely never droon but this year's drought has certainly had an effect.

We knew that the supply was slow and indeed we had been being very careful in our use of the stuff... I hadn't had a bath for all of three weeks and had taken to drinking my whisky neat. But we had no idea how low we were. The addition of an extra 100 cattle dried the well right out in one night.

It was a horrendous prospect and, as I stood in the old dairy byre being bawled at by thirty indignant stots, I got a glimpse of the agonies of stocksmen in the real droughts of the new world.

But awesome as the byreful of angry stots was, it was nothing to my other problem. We have four families living off this supply and the prospect of four modern housewives deprived of the water was too much to contemplate. Scorning a woman may be pretty hazardous, but the fury of four deprived of water for their automatic dishwashers was too much to contemplate.

I took the coward's way out. I closed the door on the stots and returned the rest of the cattle to the faraway park by the river... after all they could just come back for their check after the three days.

But I can't leave them there all winter. And, while I can live without my bath, I can't face a whole winter without water for the whisky.

24

The wince and run twitch of the Ayrshire cow

SINCE YOU'RE HERE, THERE'S ONE OR TWO WEE JOBS . . . .

30 CASTRATIONS
25 PREGNANCY DIAGNOSES
12 DISHORNINGS

GOV'T TEST

VET

Turnbull.

WE TOOK the opportunity of our compulsory herd test last week to get a free visit from the vet. The yearly test for Brucellosis and the three yearly test for Tuberculosis are the insurance against the recurrence of those two diseases now thankfully eradicated.

And when I say "thankfully" I mean thanks to the government. Of course those schemes were set up before the days of Thatcherism and self-help but they pay for everything... even the visit of the vet who comes to test for TB and to collect blood in the search for the brucella.

The chance of a free visit from the vet was too good to miss so, as well as the 39 tests, we gave him 30 castrations to do, 25 pregnancy diagnoses and 12 dishornings as well as pumping him for advice on all the eighty or so cattle to go down the race. Of course you would never organise the work that badly but if the vet had been called individually to each of those jobs I reckon the bill would have been over seven hundred pounds but I'm only to be charged for the vet's time on the farm. He was on the place for about six and a half hours over the two days and at least half of that was government time. Now I know about the Israelis putting the vets in the army along with the lawyers and the dentists (because they know how to charge) but surely he'll leave me a saving out of seven hundred.

I was sorry to see the Jerseys' horns sawn off for they were so very pretty. They were quite useful too. One little dear that I treated all summer for an eye condition used to submit totally to my ministrations as soon as I got hold of her horns. In fact if I wanted her in for treatment I could catch her and lead her in by the horns.

They were slim horns and beautifully turned but oh how savage they were with them: not to the humans but to each other.

That was particularly hard on our Ayrshire cow. She became quite paranoid about it. It was worst each morning when I gave them their magnesium cobs. No sooner would the poor old Ayrshire lower her head than she would receive a sharp horn in the rib... delivered at the run I may say. Having neither the horns nor the aggression to defend herself, the Ayrshire could only follow me and hope for the next cob to fall. But again she would be speared out of the way but the horrid Channel Islanders.

So bad did this bullying become that the poor victim developed a wince-and-run twitch. I often saw her do that when there was no opposition in sight. So the horns just had to go.

Important as the dishorning was for the victims the most important job for the herd was the pregnancy testing. Remember the very existence of this Jersey beef herd depends on their producing transplanted calves which are in no way related to their mothers. The North of Scotland College of

26

Agriculture had implanted a batch with Charolais cross Black Herefords in July and the mothers had run with our Simmental bull ever since.

According to the vet the score is Scientists 8, Bull 8. But that hardly does justice to the prowess of the bull. After all, he only got the second chance of the cows and he also successfully served three of those rejected for transplant. As my wife pointed out with just a hint of righteous indignation on his behalf "If Johnder had got the first chance there would have been precious little for the scientists to do."

The proof of the pudding is due in May.

It is when we are handling stock that I most envy my father his six full-time professional farm workers. I can handle the grain with the help of machines and contractors but with the stock there is as yet no substitute for folk. Most of my stock handling has to be done at the weekends when volunteers can be had. But vets don't do herd tests at the weekends so I had to scour the country for friends who would be both willing and available.

The squad I eventually put together was a retired motor mechanic, the chemist from the next parish, and a deep sea diver who was on his monthly two weeks holiday.

We got the job done but it was hardly a professional operation. The mechanic who had worked on the land as a boy was understandably slow, the chemist was all right until he caught his hand in the gate of the crush, and the diver didn't turn up.

The day I struck oil

I SUPPOSE the most memorable event this week was the time when I knocked the tap off the diesel tank. But as it was neither pleasant nor the best evidence of my skill as a farmer I will leave that till later.

When I came back from Kenya in the spring I had only four pedigree Simmentals and now I've some 120 cattle, and the build-up has been something of a cash-flow disaster. However the cash did start to flow uphill this week with the sale of a full load of 17 big fat stots.

I can concede a certain feeling of pride in a job well done. Continental crosses, they made a brave sight as they climbed aboard their float. But have I made any money?

They were bought at the very worst time of year when quality is hard to find and everyone has plenty of grass. They arrived on the 15th of June and with a pound a head commission for the buyer and their fare from Dingwall they cost £542 per head or 134 pence a kilo.

Immediately they were home they began to suffer as the drought really began to bite and the aftermath they were supposed to graze refused to grow. The 67 units of expensive nitrogen on their sixteen acres produced, not the usual flush of dark green but a mottled brown effect. That proved so unnutritious that I was forced to take £100 pounds worth of grazing on a piece of waste ground just to give their field a chance to get ahead.

I don't want to bore you with the details but it is fair to say that the stots never really had enough to eat all summer... until about a month ago. Then the beasts took matters into their own hands. They broke down the fence and got among the baled silage which had come off their park in the spring time.

They had a lovely feed of course and had made a terrible mess of some fifty of the bales. I patched up many of them but some were beyond repair. So the stots had a bale of silage every second day for the last month. And that worked a treat. They put on weight almost as we watched. Perhaps there would be a surplus after all.

Against that stood the banker who now needs 17.5 per-cent off a risk like me. That came to £29 a head. So that with the odd mineral block, the float to the killing house and the slaughterhouse's fees the cattle had cost £602 when they died. And the cheque will come to £617 per head.

So I had a contribution to overheads of £15 a head. As the overheads are there anyway and as you never expect to get anything for your labour in farming I was well enough pleased with that.

Especially as the government gave me an extra £29 a head called the beef special premium... I am almost rich.

And the diesel tank?

Well it happened when I was knocking down a wall between the tractor shed and the old barn. To cut a long story short, I forgot the back acter which sticks out the side. A gentle ping as we passed the diesel tank and I had my own personal oil gusher... and you've no idea the force with which 500 gallons of diesel gushes.

When my maternal grandfather's steading burnt down he invited those who came to help in for a game of billiards

while the blaze roared but I wasn't going to be so cool. I leapt off the digger and like the Little Dutch Boy stuck my hand over the broken spout. That stopped the flow but what to do next? It was no use shouting as there is no one left on the farm. My wife was due home in only four hours so I could just hang around... or maybe a travelling salesman would call. If one had he could have sold me anything.

The old brush shaft that we use to dip the tank was lying on the ground almost in reach and I figured if I could just pick it up it might fit the hole. Every move I made to get the brush led to another drenching in diesel which, you may not know, is very smelly and extremely cold.

Eventually I let the diesel flow and grabbed the brush shaft. But it didn't fit. Absolutely drookit I was back with my hand plugging the leak. I let go of my gusher again and dashed to the tree across the road. There I broke off a branch, cut it to what was not the right size, got double soaked forcing that into the hole, pulled it out and, in another all embracing spray, finally jammed it in with a bit of an old sack.

There I was in my tractor shed like a poor man's Red Adair wading in diesel. I haven't looked inside the tank to see how much I lost but it's safe to say that the profit on those stots is all away.

It's the sort of overhead you can't really plan for.

Problems of straw bonanza

THE EXTRAORDINARY fine weather continues. The grass is still growing a bit and, believe it or not, we have more grass now than we had in the drought of July. Last winter we had seventeen in-calf heifers out until March and only took them off then to give the grass time to recover for the spring leap. It looks as if this winter is going to be the same.

But just in case we get a real winter (like the ones when I was a boy) I've been doing an audit of our stocks of fodder.

I find that I have two hundred and fifty bales of silage and about twenty tonnes of moist grain. That should give me nearly two bales a day and three hundredweight of barley which should see us through till May the first... in fact, come what may, it will see us through for I will not buy in any.

But what of the straw?

Well there, there is an abundance to the point of farce.

Keen to avoid straw burning because it would be harm-ful to the ozone layer, and having been told by Mossie that it was very bad for the image of farmers to burn straw "especially on a Sunday when all the townsers come out for a run in the country", I baled the lot. So I have twelve hundred big bales of straw.

There's straw everywhere. The Dutch barn is full and so are the cattle courts...when winter does arrive at last the beasts are going to have to eat their way into the sheds. There's even a sow of sixty in the close but the bulk are in a giant triangular stack of one on two on three. It's over a hundred yards long and runs like a mediaeval fortification round the steading. When the pigeons start to fly to the oil-seed rape I rather fancy myself up there with the twelve bore and my Beau Geste hat on.

When the last thirty fat cattle go off about Christmas time. I'll only have about eighty beasts. Forty of those are spring and summer born calves and even the adults are only Jerseys which eat like church mice. And each animal will have to make muck of fifteen four-foot bales if my great fortification is to be more than just a harbour for rats.

Mind you, if they succeed I will have an even bigger problem. I was so disgusted with the spring barley this year and so pleased by the performance of the winter cereals that I sowed the whole lot this autumn. That means I have no stubble on which to put muck. But will it all go in the midden?

Ours is a traditional midden round which the traditional range of low, inconvenient and now unstable buildings are built in a square. It measures twenty-five by sixteen yards and it's half full already. If I tried to put all my twelve hundred bales of straw, twenty tonnes of barley and the two hundred and fifty bales of silage in there now it would make a pile forty feet high. I don't know what it will be by the time it has been through the cattle and had water added but by the spring day I should have a monument of organic manure. It'll be like living in the shadow of a coal bing... and while our bing may not give us pneumoconiosis it won't smell

that good.

All these big round bales would have suited my old friend Gordon Philip back from the United States on business. He left home in the fifties to seek his fortune in the wide world. But as he tells me every time he sees me, it wasn't so much the attractions of the strange lands that caused the shift as his absolute disgust at harvests which seemed to last the whole summer and autumn and where his job seemed to consist of setting up wet stooks which had blown down in the nightly monsoons.

"You can come home now Gordon", I said, "No sheaves now, just big bales which are all handled by machine." But it's too late. He's in pedigree cattle in Kansas City Missouri but he says farming over there is, like here, mainly for non-monetary rewards. Gordon Philip says he keeps on the cows for the taxable losses they make. "The future is in 'leesher'" he assures me.

Certainly his line, designing clay pigeon shooting layouts, seems to be keeping the rain out.

Now you mightn't think a few traps to fling clay doos about would take much designing but you'd be wrong. Gordon can do you a pigeon shoot where you walk through a wooded landscape where, without warning and at all kinds of angles and from all sorts of unexpected places, the doos fly like lightening across and even right at him.

I don't think my friend plays much golf though. He's designing a shooting range for

out. It's like the real thing only faster. And it can all be controlled by computer. Each shooter has a rating and logs on at the start. This means that the beginner gets birds that glide easily and slowly away from him and the crackshot is bombarded with birds catapulted a big 'leesher' complex at the moment and couldn't remember the name of his opposite number who's designing the golf course.

"Big fair haired lad. Plays a bit of golf himself."

"Jack Nicklaus," I joked.

"Yeah. That's him."

December 4, 1989

Cold comfort of the doorless digger

THERE'S BEEN a distinct change in the weather. It has been much colder and there's even been some light snow just up the road at New Deer. I'd really like to get the cows and their calves in now but I simply haven't got the water for them.

It's not that the cows or the calves would be any better off inside as yet. Though it's been cold they're doing away quite nicely for they haven't had to contend with the the driving rain that is their real enemy. And it's so dry in the fields that I can't really claim that I want them in to stop them poaching the grass.

No, I want the rest of the cattle inside to save me having to cart feed out to them. This is done with the digger, and apart from pulling turnips in the old fashioned way with a tapner, I know of no colder way of starting the day... and remember it's every day.

Of course my pal Hamish could take out straw and silage all day every day without the slightest hint of discomfort.

His digger has a quiet, heated cab with its own stereophonic radio and cassette player, and, if he feels like chatting to any of the boys or speculating on the grain futures he has the phone in the cab as well. I am thinking of giving the big man a "Teasmade" for his Christmas just to complete his comfort. Of course Hamish's digger did cost £27,000.

My digger now, it cost £2,000, and may well have been over-priced. Certainly its joys are few. It lacks a door for one thing, and that means that either going down or coming back from each run to the cows I have to bear the full force of the wind with whatever rain, hail or snow it is throwing at us. In the place where Hamish has his upholstered seat whose springs even out the roughest endrigs, I have a bare metal seat which records every pebble on the road as it is bolted straight onto the chassis.

But then I can't afford luxury. The only hope is to get some more water. So I've been finding out about that this week and really there is no problem. The water board will connect me to the mains if I get a pipe to their pipe. That's all of seven hundred yards. But with Hamish boasting that he can dig fifty yards to the hour and a keen quote for three quarter of an inch pipe I could have it done in two days for three hundred pounds... a snip surely.

I couldn't believe it would be that simple... and I was right. As I sit here I could be sipping tea made with mains water but first I must be inspected and before that can be done I must fill in a form. That arrived today and will take a fortnight to process. How long the inspector's findings will take to digest I don't know but I'm not optimistic. In the meantime I can only hope for fine weather.

I also made a start this week to sorting out the papers of my late father John R. Allan. To my delight I found that he kept a diary though only one volume has appeared so far. It includes the following reference to my early days in livestock breeding.

17.5.52 – The black and white guinea pig has produced four, all white and brown and the owner wouldn't change places with Culrossie. Later. The black guinea pig sow has produced three. This is a puzzle. Is it a case of parthenogenesis? But we remember she had five minutes beside the boar the day after her last litter was born. Seven guinea pigs in one day is big business when you are rising thirteen and guinea pigs are 4/- each. Am reminded of the days forty years ago when my grandfather and I sold homing pigeons for two shillings each. They really were homers so we were able to sell them over and over. If only we could breed a homing guinea pig.

The diary also shows him hard at work in 1952 planting trees; ash, sitka spruce, Douglas firs, silver birches, willows, and a poplar grove along the little stream that used to make its way down the brae to the river Ythan.

I remember the planting of the willows. On our brae face it was regarded as an act of strong faith or a weak mind to plant such delicate trees. And yet, though the poplars which grew well initially haven't lasted, the fine stand of willows has outlived the stream. For that is now quite dry.

We should all be grateful to the tree-planters, for they sow what they usually can not reap. And yet, as this extract from my father's journal shows, there are benefits which can accrue early to the planters of woods.

5.4.52 – When we were planting trees on the brae Bob (the orraman) and I remarked on how the Douglas firs planted four years ago were coming on. They are, some of them, seven feet tall. Bob gave a laugh and said, "Somebody's been usin' them already – for drinkin'." He picked up an empty bottle from among the trees. I didn't like to tell him who had put it there.

The deal with the water board called off

IF I had a peacock and it laid an egg in your garden, whose egg would it be? Do you remember when we were young the happy and sometimes even heated hours we spent on that one?

Of course you had to dispense quickly with the Clever Dick answers (1) It would be the Peacock's and (2) Peacocks don't lay eggs. But after that there were all sorts of interesting points of principle and of law which could be brought to bear on the problem.

Was "finders keepers" a sufficient condition for justice? And would it not be fair enough to leave the egg to the owner of the ground upon which it was laid in lieu of whatever it was that the peacock had gone there to steal in the first place? And what about the destruction of the peace and quiet caused by the act of egg-laying – anyone who has witnessed the racket a peahen makes to celebrate her

delivery of an egg would, I used to opine, be pleased to award the egg to the injured party.

I have to record that my interest in the rights to peacock's eggs ended when I went to the university. There I tried the problem as a much needed ice-breaker in the company of some budding lawyers. It was a great success as an ice-breaker but a sad disillusion to me. For the young lawyers banished the idea that justice, fairplay and what 'stood to reason' was in any way relevant to the case.

It was, as I recall, all to do with "the party of the first part being party to the party of the second part de facto or de jure, ipso facto..."

All that came back to me this week as I struggled on with my quest for water. You will recall that our well is down to a trickle and that I can't get my cattle in as I have no water for them. Worse still, I can't even get them onto the fields where the best grass is because there is no water there. And much worse than that is the fact that I have four housewives who are distinctly unamused by the lack of water in their taps and who blame me directly for the drought. I have nothing but good to say about those four women whose patience has at times verged on the saintly – incidentally they have taken to reading the *Glasgow Herald* on a Monday.

It seems such a short time since the days before this drought when I was in deep trouble with a lady neighbour who was inconvenienced by water which flowed out of my wood and onto her farm. Our dealings with her taught my wife never to make jokes about water. She tried the injured party with "Clever Charlie may be, but he can't make water run uphill. What you need is God or a plumber." We've never tried that approach again.

Last week I told you about my deal to get mains water in. This week I must tell you that the deal is off. What with the forms to be filled in, the inspections and what-not else, the pressures on me are too much. The man of action must act.

There is a field on my farm, just downhill some fifty feet, where within five hundred yards of my own well, there are no fewer than four wells. Rather than run a pipe seven hundred yards to get the mains all I have to do is run a pipe to the nearest of those wells, buy myself five hundred yards of cable and a pump and all my problems are over. Decision day was Monday and I was sure my ladies would have water on Tuesday but I told them Wednesday to be safe.

Not for the first time in my life (which can no longer be called short) my expectations, modest though they were, proved too optimistic. It's all a blur really. Delays were caused by ordering too little piping, losing one connector, the man who sold me the first pipe not being able to find it, the piping having been bought to supply all the water we needed at three quarters of an inch when, for reasons which I do not understand, it is easier for the pump to have a bigger pipe... and the motor we had got was therefore too small, the new pump's kit not containing a connector, me not understanding that you need a foot valve even if your pump is self-priming and so on. When we did get the whole

thing together we still didn't get water and that turned out to be because the foot valve was stuck in mud at the bottom of the well… and then of course, being above the ground, the whole thing froze.

Nevertheless, by Sunday we had water. The new pump had sent enough water up the hill to make our cistern overflow. The wife and I had enjoyed the luxury of a really deep bath and were trying to get out of the habit of pouring the dirty water into the cistern of the water closet.

Then the phone rang. Professional etiquette of the sort that binds doctors, priests and plumbers prohibits full disclosure of what he told me but I can tell you this. I have moved from a warm frying pan into a hellish fire. I face a revolt in the village of heroic proportions; "Charlie Allan has pinched our water".

Which brings me back to that peacock. If I have so much water that I let you dig for it and set up a well, and if I subsequently find that I need additional water myself, can I have some out of your well?

I am going to find out quickly and I'll tell you how it works out next week. I know it'll be nothing to do with common sense and everything to do with the party of the second part.

December 18, 1989

Farming with the Flu'

IT WAS all Mossie's fault.

On Sundays this most accomplished of barley barons can always be found in our most local watering hole. We lesser farmers look forward to his crack and try to wheedle out of him the secret of the five tonne crop.

Of course he never tells us anything of importance. He knows we are going to ask his advice. We know he isn't going to tell us anything and we all enjoy the game.

It was something of a disap-pointment therefore, when Mossie was missing from the discussion group last Sunday. The rest of us chatted aimlessly and played a little pool until, about half an hour late, in he came.

He wasn't looking well though. He'd got the flu', but rather than give us the chance to talk about him behind his back he had pluckily struggled down to the howff.

It was good to see him and he nearly told me how much nitrogen to put on my winter

40

wheat in March. But I could see him far enough now. A week later I am still trying to shake off his flu'.

It's been a bad week. Sore bones, sore head, dizziness and shivering with an underlying feeling of dread that something is going badly wrong on the farm.

I've never really been bothered by the flu' before. I have always found that three aspirins and half a bottle of whisky (less a nip to the wife) and I would be as right as rain in the morning. Not this time. That cure only seemed to make the headache worse.

Nothing did go badly wrong (or at least I haven't found it yet) but I did have a fairly close run thing. My fat stots are loose in what was once the dairy byre... they get barley in a walk-along trough at one side, water at one end and silage through an angle-barrier at the other. Half way along the remaining wall there is what was once the byre door and I have a gate tied across that to stop the animals and the muck bashing it out.

Well now, how I don't know, but this big red stot had got himself over the gate and jammed tight between it and the door. The door wouldn't open as it was quite jammed by the stot and the gate wouldn't open inward because of the build-up of two feet of muck.

There was no option but to dig it out despite the flu' and its attendant hangover. That was Wednesday I don't remember if I rose at all to the beasts on Tuesday.

By Friday I was well enough to think about keeping my promise to tell you how I got on investigating my rights to the wells on my farm which provide water free to my neighbours. You will recall that they flew to arms when I was seen putting a pipe down one of them.

Well the first thing I can tell you is that if someone has been taking water from a well on your land for twenty years then they have something called a prescriptive right to carry on. The landlord cannot interfere with the supply. For at least forty-five years we have been ploughing round no fewer than three wells in one twelve acre field but there is no way we could legally fill them in and straighten our furrows. It would also be illegal for me to dig a new well further up the seam and so pinch their water. The prescriptive right is to the water even before it gets to the wells.

So, you see, it is really no wonder that the good people of Methlick, when they saw me mooching round the wells on my land, reached for the fiery cross... or at least for the telephone.

I find that with such difficulties the way to get into a right mess is to employ the professionals. The sure way into resentment and fighting is to let your man-of-business in on the act. If he writes off a letter pointing out to your neighbour that "as the party of the second part is pari-passu the party of the first part..." you can safely write off any chance of an amiable settlement. No, no. The thing to do is to go to see them and talk it out. Certainly when I explained about the four women with no water and how far behind they were with the washing, and about all my thirsty beasts, they couldn't have been nicer.

Anyway I've found a well that hasn't been in use. But even if I hadn't I would have been on the right side of the law. I have a perfect right to tap into any well on my land provided that (1) there is still enough for my neighbours and (2) I do not pollute the water in any way.

When I told my wife about that she refused to believe that the law could be so sensible.

I hope next week to be fighting the elements without fighting illness as well. In the meantime I feel sufficiently recovered to venture down to the tavern to see if Mossie will tell me how to grow two tonnes of rape. I don't suppose he will but I might just be able to give him his flu' back.

It's not all gloom and doom

I DON'T know why everyone takes stock at the beginning of the year. The first of January is just a day like any other. Hardly anyone has a financial year that begins then. You can't even say, as our fathers could, that the harvest was all sold and next year's seeds still in the bag. In fact as the year starts we have already sown all our crops for 1990.

I suppose the reason we tend to have a count up at the turn of the year is that it is a very easy date to remember though it may not be that easy to remember exactly what happened on it.

Certainly my great grandfather John Yull could have been excused if he remembered little of the new year of 1894. The records of the local general merchants (John Grant of Methlick) show that the tenant of Little Ardo bought two gallons of aqua (as the water of life was called somewhat coyly) on Hogmanay. But that had not been sufficient unto the night

and he was back the next morning for another gallon.

This fact, important as it is to the social history of the North East of Scotland, would not have come to light had it not been that John Yull bought that lochan of whisky on account... and he only paid his bill at the term.

The current keeper of the supermarket that was once John Grant's shop has, I'm delighted to say, kept up the tradition of half yearly accounts and he does so with a good grace. But I don't know how he would react if the current farmer of Little Ardo went in on Hogmanay for twelve bottles, got another six on new year's day and came in to pay for them on the 28th of May.

Anyway I'm afraid the family blood has been too far diluted. John Yull would be ashamed of his great grandson. I don't know that I could even go along with the sage who said "whisky comes in an awkward sized bottle... too much for one but not nearly enough for two". Certainly I find that I either need a hand with a bottle of whisky or a hand with my work the next day.

Of course, even in my family, there are more yardsticks of honour than capacity to remain insufficiently refreshed by large quantities of liquid re-

least my forefathers can't look down and point the finger at me for not being well on with the spring work.

The 50 acres of oilseed rape varies from magnificent to O.K. but Mossie says it doesn't matter what it looks like at this time of year. The early sown winter barley is looking good

freshment. So how is the rest of my stewardship of the family farm going as we enter the nineteen-nineties?

I walked the fields and went over all the stock with just that question in mind at the end of the old year and I have to say that I wasn't that proud of what I saw.

The crops are young yet so it may be early to judge but at

though there is a bit of mildew which I am assured is under the control of the sprays. The later stuff looks fine but not nearly thick enough to form its own microclimate to help it through if we get this bad winter some are predicting. And the same goes for the wheat which looks very sparse and pathetic but it has only been in the ground for nine weeks.

The cattle are healthy though I am in constant fear of the odd cough turning into a scourge for our calves. But they are a poor show for ancestors. John Yull's father William got a medal for the best shorthorn bull at the Ebrieside show in 1872 and he would think my beef cows a rum lot. They're the Jerseys I bought for double suckling transplanted beef calves and it has to be said that while some of the calves have done well the cows do look as though they would dearly love to return to the Channel Islands.

In 1970 I formed one of the founding herds of British Simmental Cattle here and produced two Perth Champions and won at the Highland Show as well. Now all that remains of that is one good cow, one good heifer, a heifer calf that might be good and a bull calf which has not yet been castrated. I once was the proud owner of over seven hundred cattle on this farm and today there are only just over a hundred.

But you mustn't think that it is all gloom as we enter another decade. For I have not been the only man to take stock of the activities on Little Ardo. We have a financial controller who comes four times a year to tell me how badly I am doing and what the implications are of all my ideas to improve matters. He says I am making a profit. It's still not a six percent return on the landlord's and tenant's capital invested in the farm but it is enough to live on... especially for a man who is too busy working to spend much.

My financial whizz-kid is so pleased with me that he thinks I should be employing a man but I haven't the courage for that. Still I was very chuffed to be told as much.

Indeed when my wife was trying to get me to stop working the other day she threatened me with the Great Reaper. I was full enough of myself to tell her that for the profitable farmer of Little Ardo nothing less than a combined harvester would do. To that my daughter Susie, who is also a bit full of herself these days having started her first job on a national Sunday paper, said, "They'll more likely send a muckspreader for you Dad".

There's a "tak doon" for ye.

All show no dough theory

I'VE HAD another setback and again it's down to Mossie. I don't mind him having the reputation of being the best cereal grower in the district and I don't grudge him his success. But why won't he share his wisdom? What's the point of telling us what we are doing wrong all the time without telling us what we should be doing?

The latest example is the oilseed rape and the pigeons. The war is continuing. We're ready for them each morning, Willie and I, and so far we seem to be keeping them heading off to our neighbours pretty well. We're not shooting that many because, much to Willie's disgust, I keep shooting on sight... from the hip even... rather than let them land.

It's a time-consuming business at the moment with an effective flying time of about seven hours a day. But what's it going to be like in March when food is really scarce and it's light at the back of six in the morning?

I was floating my ideas along those lines at the discussion group that meets at the local tavern on Sunday evenings and hoping for Mossie's views... and I got them. "You're wasting your time", was the sages verdict. "The worse your rape's lookin' now the better it'll yield at harvest... All show no dough".

Now even a farmer with my track record should be able to have his crops looking bad at any given time of year so it can hardly be as simple as that. I was suspicious... after all Mossie does have the noisiest banger in the countryside. I refer, of course, not to his car but to the gas gun that threatens his neighbours windows every ten minutes or so.

And yet there does seem to be something in the "all show no dough" theory. Certainly I had a crop which last year was eaten absolutely bare in Janu-

ary while the other was virtually unscathed. And yet the eaten field gave 30 hundredweights at harvest time to 28 hundredweights on the other. Of course nothing is ever that simple for we gave the badly mauled field a massive dose of foliar feed in the spring to help it recover. On the other hand, the field that was ignored by the pigeons was by far the better field.

Another neighbour, Rothiebrisbane, had the far end of a field stripped while the side near the road was untouched. At harvest time he got his two combines to take four bouts each, one from one end and the other from the other. The whole field had had identical treatment except for the attention of the vermin. And lo! The yield was one ton at either end.

Then there's Lindsay Cook who has always been something of a figure of fun because he never did anything to discourage the dove of destruction. He's taken that approach one stage further this year and let his sheep loose on the rape.

He's continued to do what our forefathers did in putting the sheep on the winter wheat in the backend. He says that helps the tillering of the cereals as well as being a very tasty bite for the lambs. But he says that the mild winters we've been having have made it even more advantageous to let the sheep on the cereals.

During these mild winters it hasn't just been the crops that have grown, so has every fungus known to agronomists. The mild winter of 1989 cost farmers who bothered as much as an extra £20 an acre in fungicides. But not Lindsay Cook. He put the sheep on to eat the mildew. He reckons that saves him at least one spray a year and being a form of biological control it's environmentalist-friendly.

So what are we to do? Well, like many people in this part of the world, I employ a crop consultant and my worrying about such questions as these may be a bit like keeping a dog and barking yourself. He could hardly agree with the all show no dough theory... and he doesn't. He wants me to have as much back-end growth as possible and keep it healthy all the way to harvest. He says that grazing it down is a bad idea because in a severe winter you need a lot of growth there to create the crop's own microclimate.

I've no doubt that will be right but where are the severe winters these days... wet ones yes but when last did we have a whole month's frost? And I think I've spotted patches in one field which illustrate the Mossie theory well. Due to a malfunction in the sowing machine we have areas in one field which are really a riot of growth. But on close inspection what we have is a lot of tall rather weak looking plants... can easily see the sparser areas yielding more in the end of the day.

So you see I am feeling my way to a new policy for next autumn. I intend to try half as many seeds, no backend nitrogen and a more tolerant attitude to the pigeons. I would consider grazing a few sheep on the winter crops but for the experience this year of Lindsay Cook. When he opened the gate for his 250 lambs the phone rang every few minutes as delighted neighbours phoned up to tell him his sheep had broken into the rape.

Abject Roadside Farming

THERE IS nothing so lightens the eye in Aberdeenshire as the sight of a neighbour's crop which has gone flat. Many's the time my father had to make a detour to see the particularly splendid stand of thistles that Hilly was growing on the glebe or the mess Collynie's cattle had made when they got in among the barley.

For that reason and because he objected to giving his neighbours that sort of pleasure the old man advised me always to farm well beside the road.

Perhaps, therefore, it is just as well he's been gathered-in now for over the holiday I provided the good people of Methlick with a splendid example of abject roadside farming. On the afternoon of Hogmanay I stuck my precious digger right in the middle of the field that overlooks the village. It had to stay there until the third of January when I finally got a mechanic sober enough to come and sort out the trouble... dirt in the diesel.

As you can imagine I got little sympathy from Fiona. When I told her I said, "and they'll all be saying 'aye I doubt Charlie must have had a fair nicht last nicht'".

"Well he did didn't he?" she said with just a hint of aggression.

Mind you there was no need of me as an object of the scorn of the countryside. For the New Year has seen the opening of the first new auction mart to be built in the North East since the war and well beyond. At a time when livestock marketing is a declining fashion and when they themselves are pioneering a new system of computerised selling, Aberdeen and Northern Marts has just spent some four million pounds on a massive new mart on a greenfield site.

Thainstone near Inverurie has four and a half acres under one single span roof. It can pen 3000 cattle or 11000 sheep

though I can find no one except those who decided to build the new complex who believes it will ever have to. Certainly the 800 sold on the first day were in danger of getting lost… especially as the ventilation system wasn't working and the breath of the cattle created a dense fog over the handling area. At it's worst you couldn't see the far end of the shed... but then that was a long way away.

To the delight of those who came to sneer, the fancy electronic scoreboard didn't work and the weights had to be chalked up on the blackboard somebody had had the foresight to bring with him from one of the abandoned marts.

The shareholders in Aberdeen and Northern Marts criticised every aspect of their investment. It was too cold at the front of the rings and too hot at the back. The gates didn't work properly and the passageways were difficult to clean. The food was far too expensive, the bars weren't ready yet let alone open and the steps at the sale arenas were too steep for anyone over fifty.

There were only two criticisms I didn't hear. No one said the new mart was too small. And no one said it was ugly, uninviting and an unpleasant place to be. But then, as Prince Charles so rightly observed, we don't worry about things like that.

There was a time when the cattle fattener's week took him to Ellon Market on Monday, to Turriff on Tuesday, Maud on Wednesday, and Aberdeen on Friday. Maud survives for the moment but for the rest it will be Thainstone every day and we will be the poorer in a social sense for that. And the small towns that have lost their market day have lost something of great historical and cultural importance.

So perhaps the deluge of abuse that has fallen upon the new venture was no more than was to be expected and perhaps it is fitting that those who would abolish our traditions should run a gauntlet of scepticism. But I suspect that from the point of view of the shareholders the decision to sweep away the small markets into a new monster will emerge as a triumph.

For at Thainstone they are building much more than a new Mart... it is to be an Agricultural Centre no less. All the space in the present development has been taken for offices, showrooms (and of course banks) and there is pressure from the trade to press on with stage two. The new Mart has been built on a five hundred acre farm and the plan is to develop that as demand from the agricultural supply trade dictates and the word is that there is a scramble for space there too.

And why should it stop at supply? What about downstream agricultural activity. Thainstone might even one day be the centre of the local food processing industry.

But for now it is just a muckle mart and the subject of dogs' abuse. As he looked down at the mass of concrete and steel in the store ring on the first day, the farmer sitting next to me said, (and I translate) "look how hard it is besides the timber at Maud." and then to no one in particular "Maybe, like the Berlin Wall, it'll all be chipped away". I might wish it so but I doubt it.

Aversion therapy applied

I TOLD you some time ago about my trip to Jersey to buy some cows upon which to found what I believed would be a unique herd of Channel Island hill cows. I got the last six at a herd dispersal sale and then set off round the farms to see if I could pick up some more. It's one of those about which I want to tell you today.

At one of the better herds on the Island where they don't often have to sell at below four figures I was offered a tiny, skinny calf which I judged to be about six months old. The story was that this beastie was in fact nearer a year, and despite her only being about three hundredweight, she had had a night out with the bull and was thought to have become in calf. As a result of that she was unlikely to grow into a fine big cow and would always let the herd down. So the farmer would let her go despite her excellent pedigree etc. etc... I tell you those Jersey farmers have nothing to learn from the Irish cattle dealers.

As I had been trying to get back into the swing of the beef cattle business after my three years in Africa I determined to try to buy her for a pound a kilo and though I had to go a bit more in the end I was astonished to find myself the owner of this prize at £250... pounds delivered to Methlick.

I wasn't quite so surprised when I noticed that my prize had a not altogether attractive additional feature... she had a badly twisted face. I wasn't unduly worried mind, and in the drought this summer her twist allowed her to get a number of tasty bites round the side of the trough and at the back of the gate which were unavailable to her more correct sisters.

Apart from my trying to steer the odd visitor past her, Lottie (short for Lautrec) was more or less ignored at Little Ardo until January the sixteenth when she was delivered of quite the smallest calf I have ever seen. It died soon after it was born which may have been a loss to Lottie (though she never showed it) but it was no loss to me, as Jersey bull calves have no value here.

She had a fine bag of milk so it was with a lightsome heart that I slipped over to Maitland Mackie's place for a couple of Limousin bull calves. No wonder those dairy boys are making the money. They make a profit on their milk and they have calves at as much as two hundred pounds a cow as a free bonus. I was paying five pounds a kilo for calves for my pound a kilo cow.

Anyway Lottie seemed quite impressed with the calves but took a very narrow-minded view of what they tried to do next. Whenever either of them got near a teat she would move smartly off. So I tied her up. Then she learned to kick. That had the desired (by Lottie) effect and the calves became very reluctant to risk suckling.

So I had to manhandle the calves in-about to the cow and that gave me two insights. First, I was reminded of the problems of getting a terrified horse to drink after you have taken him to the water. And then I was reminded that the Limousin breed has a reputation for nervousness.

They say that the best way to separate Limousin cows from their calves at weaning is to put

53

them in a pen with a six foot fence. You then let off both barrels of the twelve bore and the cows all jump out of the pen.

Well, of course, I don't really believe that but certainly those two calves were scary devils. A gentle nudge towards the cow was enough to send them bolting forward and taking hold of them to force a teat into their mouths led to complete panic. So I just had to have patience and let them find their own way there.

That they eventually did after which it was just a case of dealing with the kicking in the traditional way... with aversion therapy. Every time the cow kicked the calves I caned the cow.

This is not my favourite job and, as one who was brought up without corporal punishment and to believe it was wrong, I can't do it without being beset with guilt. But I know of no other way with cows and the penalties of failure would be high.

Three days it took. The final breakthrough came when I changed the subject of my chastisement. I noticed that as she became more used to the thrice daily ritual, the cow took to kicking only when the calves banged their heads up into her udder to release more milk. So instead of caning the cow when she kicked, I started on the calves when they banged.

They proved to be quick learners and now the scene is idyllic. The two calves sleep beside their foster mother most of the day in an effort to make room for the next sloshing of milk at 5.% butterfat and Lottie chews her cud with the air of one who recognises a job well on the way to being well done.

I'm really looking forward to watching the progress of the three and I'm thinking of making a book on how long it takes for the calves to reach their mum's body-weight. She can't be 250 kilos when she's been sucked, so that day could easily be as early as August.

If it is, then Lottie will look like my star buy of 1989, twisted face or no.

Dazzling show of gluttony at the Green Week

IT IS a wonderful thing to write for the *Glasgow Herald*. Or so it seems to me for I've been to Berlin at the invitation of the West German government... and the invitation was sent to me at the Albion Street offices.

The occasion was the annual Green Week in which half a million Germans guzzle their way round more than twenty acres of food and drinks from fifty-seven countries. It's a consumer show not an agricultural one and is in fact a most dazzling display of gluttony.

There is an ocean of wine from everywhere outside the polar circles, mountains of German sausages, Polish pork,

Israeli fish, Kenyan fruit and Irish beef. In fact the Irish did particularly well here. Not only were they selling their beef steaks to a never-ending queue in their own hall, but they also hi-jacked our hall.

The British effort was pronounced "excellent" by our senior agriculture minister John Selwyn Gummer but that was a minority view. The journalists who had been to the Green Week before would only say that it wasn't as bad as usual. Certainly the farm gate component of what was on offer was very small. There was a shop busy selling two hundred and eighty brands of Scotch whisky but you get an awful lot of whisky from a tonne of grain. There was a very high class sweetie shop and a good and fairly popular baked tattie stall. But the real success of the "British" effort was the English Pub which stocked only Glenfiddich, Malibu, gin Pimms and Guinness. They were busy but the only thing I saw sold there was Guinness. And while all that was going on, the cafe across the way couldn't keep up with the demand for Irish coffee.

However the whole consumer bonanza was put in context by the middle-aged couple, wearing sensible but ill-fitting clothes, eating the sausage sandwiches they produced from their old-fashioned shopping bag. To this celebration of capitalism's triumph in food marketing they brought their own sandwiches.

For they are among the 200,000 East Germans expected to cross the Berlin wall during the ten days of the exhibition to see for themselves how the other half live now. They can look and they can wonder, but they can't afford to buy anything.

In my four days in Berlin I must have listened to a dozen speeches saying what a wonderful thing it is that the wall is coming down, and I've no doubt that it is. I even did my bit to help. And better than that I got an Irish journalist to act as my navvy. He borrowed a pick from an East German guard and under my supervision gouged us out pieces from the Eastern side of the wall.

Our West German guide told us that a couple of months ago the same guard would have shot us.

Of course it is wonderful that that is past, but our West German friends don't seem to realise that we may not find it quite as wonderful as they do.

Part of my introduction to Berlin was a handout proclaiming Berlin as a great place for childhood memories to flood in. Very true but no-one seemed to realise that the childhood memories that would flood in to me would be of sitting round my grandfather's wireless each evening at six and cheering as Alvar Nadall told us how uncle George and his pals were getting on trying to knock six bells out of the place.

It is said that on one tour of Berlin the journalists were told that this building had been put up by an international effort. The Americans had put up so many million marks and even the French had paid for a large chunk of it, but, unfortunately the British hadn't contributed at all. In what must be one of the less tactful remarks in the annals of human history, one hack protested that the British had indeed made an important contribution. "We levelled the sight for you."

You may or may not find that funny but I'm sad that my long memory spoiled my trip to some extent. I'd like to go back though for there is much to see and to wonder at.

Like the Unter den Linden, the Princess Street of Berlin, enough of which remains or is being restored to allow the possibility that it can once again become one of the architectural wonders of the world.

And at the Green Week I was particularly taken with the Beef Hall. There, fifteen breeds including the Aberdeen Angus, Galloways, Highlanders and Luings were on display. When I was there the Galloways seemed to win an inter-breed team event with a group led by a twenty-one hundred-weight bull who must have smelt the Scottish air at one time, for he was called Dalswinton Nobleman.

There was in the Beef Hall a sobering clue as to the German thinking on the future for farming. The education effort was directed to explaining the roles of three types of cattle; dairy, beef and "breeds kept mainly to maintain the landscape".

I'm afraid the British breeds were mostly in the last category.

Potential for green stones

I'VE BEEN giving some thought to the need for me to do a bit of diversifying. Everyone is exhorting us to diversification, whether it's to help to make us less efficient to reduce the over-capacity of our industry or to keep a few swains in the countryside so that townies can have something to look at when they venture forth at weekends.

But for reasons that I don't understand and for the first time in my life, I find that I have no financial necessity to do anything with my farm except farm it and isn't that just as it should be? Is it not the most abominable kick in the teeth to tell the proud practitioners of our only truly essential industry, the one without which we would all surely die, that they must not only produce our food but do beds and breakfasts and make nature trails of our farms as well?

Still, I feel we have to do something if only to be able to make a positive response when asked at polite parties what we are doing to diversify... it goes along with conservation, and apart from trying to conserve some of my rape crop from the wood pigeons, I'm not doing anything about that either.

I have a neighbour who is making a very big thing of the shooting. He charges a king's ransom for a day's mayhem among a wall to wall carpet of hand-reared pheasants. Oscar Wilde who described foxhunting as the unspeakable in pursuit of the inedible would surely have had a field day with that lot.

You might think my neighbour's next step would be shooting fish in a barrel. But, in fact, it's a truly wonderful scheme which will help us all. It is a miracle of modern marketing. While I am trailing around my fields for half of every day trying to keep the pigeons off the oil seed rape this man is charging rodent control technicians who prefer to call themselves sportsmen, £60 pounds a day for the privilege. Apparently they're queuing up.

When my wife heard about that she was very excited. Apart from the pigeons there are all sorts of things we want rid of and would gladly charge people to do away with. Her idea was to go into Pick Your

bricks.

But I thought something in the bloodsports line would be a readier seller and I thought I had cracked it when I was taking a tractor wheel to the village the other day.

For forty-five years I have walked and driven down to Methlick and wherever possible have stopped to watch the trout playing above the bridge

Own with our annual crop of stones. We've always had a few people who wanted some for a rockery or the foundations for their garage, but Fiona would go into P.Y.O. in a big way and she would sell our stones as "green". They would save the earth's scarce resources that are squandered making cement blocks and

over the Ythan. There are always some and as a child I spent hours with my face against the steel rails watching.

It was there that I did my first scientific experiment. I had been told that if you lick frozen steel your tongue will stick and you won't ever get it off. Well I couldn't resist putting that ridiculous theory to the test on a very cold February morning and found to my horror that my tongue did in fact stick absolutely. It was a tricky situation. When you are caught by the tongue it is hard to call for help and when one is in such an indelicate position it is tempting not to draw attention to it. Eventually I must have warmed the bridge up sufficiently for it to let go but I was left with a very sore tongue and a reluctance towards experimentation.

Most of my times at the bridge were happier of course and on several occasions I saw eels inches thick and maybe four feet long but till last week I never saw a salmon. But then from the seat of my tractor there they were, two of them just above the bridge.

So there's my diversification. Those salmon are on the three hundred yards of the Ythan which I own. Everyone else on the river sells tickets and makes a nice little earner out of the fishers who come and flay the burn with their expensive equipment. And they say the burn is full of fish this year.

It's not as full as it once was if you believe the old men. They'll tell you that when they were young they could walk across the river on the backs of the fish, but that the silage effluent and netting at the rivermouths have spoiled things. Certainly something has, for there used to be a rule on the farms round here that the farmers weren't allowed to feed the single men salmon more than three times a week... and the men insisted on that.

So I was all set to have the tickets printed.

But then the wind rattled at my window as it will for those who farm the lands of their ancestors. I remembered what my father, John R. Allan, had said when we were discussing the privatisation of the Ythan fishings in 1950. I don't remember the words exactly and he was such a beautiful speaker that I don't want to make them up, but what he meant was this. The fishing doesn't belong to us any more than the river does. The water is just passing down through our land and the fish are just passing us on their way up. We have no control over either and have no natural right to stop anybody taking the fish.

He liked to be asked for a day's fishing but never asked a fee. I don't know if I share his view but that diversification can wait.

My beef with the TV channels

AS A farmer of beef cattle my main feeling this week is of dismay at the sheer unfairness of the television treatment of my livelihood. For the first time in living memory the beef price was lower at Christmas than it was in September and that cost me a lot of money. And the price has fallen steadily since.

A lot of that loss can without a doubt be put down to one cow. I refer to that poor brute which has staggered about on all channels nightly for what has seemed an age. It is horrible and it is so unfair. What possible point can there be in showing us that dreadful sight over and over again every time the subject of mad cow disease comes up?

No human has yet suffered from this disease but millions have died of cancer. Why do the televisors not show someone dying of cancer every time that disease is mentioned? I believe it is because that would be painful and shocking as well as gratuitous. But is it not painful and shocking to we who care for the nation's farm animals to have that poor mad cow thrust at us nightly? And isn't it entirely gratuitous?

It was also quite unfair that the BBC's alarmist *Focal Point* programme, as well as reporting their quite proper brief on concerns about human health, used yard after yard of film showing cows being shot, disembowelled and hung up in a slaughterhouse. There is no way that what goes on in a slaughterhouse is pleasant viewing, and it may be a legitimate subject for a film on just that. But it is gratuitous to include those scenes in a film about mad cow disease. People are concerned about their health and may watch the programme because of that. But the same people may well prefer, like the rest of us, to turn off when it comes to watching the moment of death.

And the damnable thing is we have done so much to safeguard the public who eat our food and the welfare of the animals involved. I've just been to Berlin where I saw pork sausages from Poland sold on unmade waste ground off old newspapers and bits of cloth which weren't very dirty. Before that I was in Africa where cows are still clubbed to death.

No doubt there are still things to be done but please, film-makers, take one thing at a time and stick to the point at issue. Be fair.

There is little doubt the issue is going to cost me money. The day after the *Focal Point* programme, my wife who works in town, heard a graduate colleague discussing with a friend how she should dispose safely of the pound of mince she had in the refrigerator.

It's an ill wind that blows nothing but ill though, and it may just be that exaggerated fears for farmed foods may be helping me in the war I'm waging to keep the wood-pigeons in the wood or in the air or at least on oil seed rape belonging to my neighbours.

My local game dealer can't keep up with the demand for pigeons both from the continent and from here in Britain. He is getting five to ten thousand a week just now and could sell more. John Bain says the attractions of the cushet include the fact that it is naturally fed and that it must be in perfect health when it is shot... if they get ill they drop dead.

For whatever the reason he has raised the price to 35 pence per bird which means that "sportsmen" can have their fun for nothing and that the judicious hunter can make himself a nice little earner if he can get onto a flight path of pigeons.

On the other hand it's a good wind that blows nothing but good. Because the price is so high I've lost Willie my hunter. He's got fed up of shooting at Little Ardo because I have been so successful in scaring the pests away. Just as he is getting set to let the encroaching hoards have it with both barrels I am sure to appear waving my arms and firing in the air to scare them off.

And even when I am not there I have a dozen scarecrows in each field and have left all my mobile machinery as well as two immobile cars in the fields to make it look as though there are men around. Mossie asked me if I was having a roup that I had dragged all my machinery out to the parks. "And would it nae be handier to have all the items in the same park?"

For all that I am not beating the pigeons. I would say that two of my fifty acres have been eaten but not yet so badly that they won't recover on the spring day.

For that I should thank Big Hamish. He hasn't got round to doing anything about the pigeons and they have duly given him an unfair share of their trade. Of course his digger being worth £27,000 he felt he couldn't leave it out in the field. My old wreck, on the other hand, with its front bucket up and the back-acter fully extended looks to the woodies like a great steel bird of pray.

Well well, Hamish's rape park gradually turned brown until now it is just like a ploughed field with tramlines. But still the pigeons go there working underground to extract the last root. He must be the cheeriest man I know for his reaction is that he's going to put the hat round his neighbours for the favour he's done us all.

I am grateful to him of course, but I'm not going to put anything in till I see how much I'm going to lose on the beef job.

Giovanna and the weatherman

He promised us a seed time and a harvest,
But he never promised what they would be like.

THAT SPLENDID couplet from the pen of Borders Farmer poet Tim Douglas illustrates well the farmer's perennial dilemma of whether to do whatever it is before things get worse or wait till things get better.

The immediate problem is whether or not the time has come for the application of the first nitrogen of Spring. I'd prefer to wait for the first cuckoo but my crops specialist says now is the time. But what if we get a return to real weather and it all gets trapped under a foot of snow and leaches quietly down to the sea when the thaw comes in April?

Of course there are people who have no other job than to try to keep us right on the future course of the weather but unfortunately their record in consulting the entrails is not reassuring. What happened to the prediction that this February would be the worst for snow and icy blast since 1963? We've had an inch or so that lasted about three days.

Of course there has been a lot of wind in some parts of the country but there's been nothing in the North East Corner. There was the very pretty girl called "Trish" who appears with "John" on the midday news on Channel 4 telling us that for the fourth Thursday in a row we were to have terrible gales... and it was a fine breezie day here.

It all reminds me of the dreadful wet spring of 1977 when I was on the phone daily to the local weather men here. It was April and we'd run short of keep so the cows had to go out though there was no grass for them. In their search for sustenance the old dears soon had what little green there was turned to brown. They say that when it's really wet cows eat with five mouths and it was certainly true that Spring.

It was into that world that Giovanna was born. I found her one particularly dismal morning in a puddle.

You may well think Giovanna a pretentious name for a calf but she was a Romagnola and her mother had been imported from Italy. How happy she would have been in her mother's home in Masseratta. She was well enough in Scotland, but cold and miserable.

Now we have a theory that if you take such a calf inside it is liable to pneumonia so if at all possible we would leave her outside. I would phone the very willing weather-men at Dyce. If the bad weather was to last we'd take Giovanna in but if it would clear up soon we'd leave her out.

I got the news I wanted. The rain would peter out overnight and the sun would shine on my new calf in the morning.

However the next day the rain was still teeming down and the little thin-skinned calf was cowering and shivering beside the dyke. I phoned the weatherman again. Ah yes, the rain was clearing from the south and the fine weather would be in Buchan by dinnertime.

The rain in the afternoon was, if anything, heavier but my expert insisted it was clearing from the south and that it would be a fine morning. Giovanna was left to her watery fate.

Day three dawned to a cascade. I phoned the met office again. It was clearing from the south and the sunshine had already reached Dundee.

On the morning of the fourth day it was still raining but I was no longer worried for my calf. When I went out she was what I call chundering. That's a sort of excited galloping on the spot, and it's a sure sign of ruddy good health. Giovanna had known nothing but rain and was thriving and determined to enjoy life whatever.

All the same I was intrigued to hear what the weatherman was saying. Again it was clearing from the south and he was expecting the sun in a couple of hours.

Without rancour and in the spirit of scientific enquiry I explained that this was my fourth day of phoning and that I had heard it all before. "In fact," I said, "looking out of my window I can't see that lot stopping for a week."

"Well, that's what it says

here", said my friend. And then. "Hold on till I have a look outside." After a minute he came back and said, "Aye, I see what you mean. That rain'll be on all day."

There is no earthly reason why we should blame the weathermen for their failure to predict the weather. What expert can do anything expertly? Can your doctor do anything about your bad back? I used to be an expert in something called economics. I was consulted for high fees on all manner of things. The official secrets act and professional confidence prevents me from giving you examples of the mistakes I made. What I can tell you is that, to a man, economic experts foretold a world-wide depression after Hitler's war and in fact we had the longest boom in the history of human endeavour.

I have a friend who was once a weather forecaster in East Africa and for an experiment he threw away his charts and simply forecast that the weather tomorrow would be the same as today's. It wasn't foolproof, of course, but he did get better results with far less effort.

And I've decided to act on that principle. I'm going to assume that this Winter is going to be like last year's. That there will be enough warmth to get the crops moving steadily towards another splendid harvest. To that end the manure goes on.

Making a pound out of the doo-run run

DESPITE WHAT I said last week I still haven't got the nitrogen on the oil seed rape though I have got a dusting on the winter barley. The trouble is the wind which seems to blow every day. It hasn't been the sort of roaring gale that tore the roofs off last February but just enough to make it finer to stay indoors and postpone anything that can be postponed.

The problem is that if you put on your manure in a wind it spreads unevenly. That gives you uneven growth and all your neighbours know that you sowed it when you shouldn't... or they may suggest that you were fou' when you did it.

No one really knows when the optimum time to apply the fertiliser is but I am anxious to get the rape growing as soon as possible to beat the pigeons. For some reason they don't like to land in fields where the rape is tall. They really like a nice open field like the ones they have grazed well down already. So I want mine to grow on and consolidate the lead I have over those who have lost more to the blue hordes.

There are just too many pigeons to make shooting any use on an individual farm basis. So the pigeon war is now being fought between farmers rather than against the cushets. Certainly we've given up all pretence of shooting to kill. All we do is scare then off every hour or so. That's called the "doo-run". You jump into the car and drive to the first field and let off the twelve bore. If any rise you let them have the second barrel then set off in the car and drive down through the other two fields blaring the horn. If there are any pigeons you jump out and let off both barrels to send them on their way to someone else's fields.

It's all a bit futile. How

much better if we really could get together and reduce their numbers. And I've had a letter from reader who has a plan. Why don't I get a rocket propelled net and once there are a few hundred grazing, fire the rocket and trap the lot?

I got very excited when I read this suggestion and even more so when I discovered that the Aberdeen University scientists were using that method to trap geese just ten miles from here in the Ythan estuary. They, I discovered, have caught several hundred geese at a firing. This was surely the answer. And it might even pay as, at 35 pence a head, I would get £350 every time I trapped a thousand doos.

As you may have guessed my optimism didn't survive subsequent research.

The first snag is that the police insist on a firearms certificate for this weapon. And you can see why. The shot that carries the net over the unfortunate birds weighs over three pounds and has more in common with a mortar than with a tupenny squib. Apparently there is a famous case when one got detached from the net and flew half a mile off, even crossing a motorway.

Then you have to get a li-cence to use your net to catch birds and for that you have to prove that what you are doing is in the interests of science. I doubt if protecting my oilseed rape would count as a scientific project.

And then, most damaging of all, it is illegal to use nets to trap birds in order to kill them. Apparently it is all right to shoot them but illegal to use a net. That does seem odd really as the net is more humane... after all a bird is either caught or it isn't whereas the tragedy of shooting is those that are hit but get away.

In any case I don't really think the nets they use for the geese would do for the pigeons. Although they can be as long as you like, the nets are only some five metres wide so you have to get pretty close to the quarry. They are ideal for ducks which graze a narrow strip of shore. But the only way to get geese is to bate the trap, wait till they have got thoroughly used to feeding there and then pounce. We might put down grain for the cushets, and no doubt they would come to the trap eventually but it would mean leaving them undisturbed for days. And days of undisturbed grazing on my rape they are not going to get.

Another reader asks me about the economics of the pigeon war. Well how's this for economy? Brucklay Estate, whose cushet-doos reach here when the winds are right, are making a fortune out of shooting them when they return. They are charging £60 per gun for sportsmen to sit in the tree-tops in specially constructed towers to shoot the birds when they come in to roost. And the guns are queuing up. Last week I even met a party of pigeon-shooters over from America. It is nothing for a gun to knock a hundred down in a session and that would be another £35 to the estate.

I do have a small wood... I wonder how much it would cost to build a tower... or two?

March 12, 1990

Muck was the only profit

THE NITROGEN is on the rape and the winter barley and a tinge of bright new green is appearing on the fields. Even the grass, which has been remarkably green all winter, has taken on a hint of freshness. Soon I'll have to get Willie (our once-a-week gardener) out of his hibernation to cut the lawn.

It is such harbingers of Spring that traditionally turn a young man's fancy to love and an old farmer's to buying some cattle for the grass. In fact the Spring madness, which takes the young things, the pheasants, the rooks, the herons and the hares in March, is mirrored in the store cattle rings all over the country.

The first stirrings are there already. Backwoodsmen who haven't been seen at the ringside since last Spring start appearing, making a few tentative bids and drifting off to hear the news, or consult the salesmen on the possibility of getting a few last minute tons of fertilisers at last October's price.

There's not an awful lot to buy yet. Everybody here about has plenty of winter keep. But gradually as the month goes on, more and more cattle will come out of the houses where they have been stored all Winter as farmers see the end of the silage pit looming. And in April they'll be cascading onto the market because there's nothing left in the barns... or because the banker is looking hard for the Spring day.

And, of course, as time goes on the buyers get keener. As it gets nearer and nearer to turn-out time the grazier can be surer and surer of having enough to keep them inside long enough to give the grass a head's start. Graziers have bank accounts too. At 17 or 18 per-cent the longer you can get someone else to store your grazers the better.

So the trickle of seasonal interest in the stores just now will build up to a stampede for cattle in April as farmers face the prospect of grass growing out of control and nothing to eat it. The markets will then be in the grips of a Spring madness just as strong as any that turned a young man's fancy.

So the question I have been asking myself is "should I join in and try to buy myself some grazers... and if so when?" My good friend James Fowlie, whose family have been masters of finishing cattle for at least three generations, says "Nae yet onyway. You'll get them dear in April". That's true of course, but the trouble is that though they may not be cheap just now it will be unusual if they aren't dearer when the grass really starts to get going.

So how did my efforts as a fattener serve me last year? Well I had been out of the store market for three years or more and I was so appalled at how mad the Spring madness had become that I bought the ugliest Ayrshire steer I have ever seen for £350 (a pound a kilo) and quickly found me a tenant for the grass. The £50 an acre seemed good money compared with spending £1000 an acre to stock it.

After the silage was off I did get bolder and bought 23 stots for £542 a head. They went fat off the grass at an average (after killing and transport expenses) of £617 a head which left me a net profit of £15 after deducting for bank expense and fertilisers. Hardly a fortune, you may think, even with the government's kind contribution of £29; the beef special premium.

Emboldened by the excellent harvest I then bought thirteen stores for feeding up for Christmas. They cost £567 and sold for £624. That gave me a margin of £57 to pay for the ten pounds of barley a day, and the ad-lib straw and silage they had eaten.

Had that been all my cattle finishing for last year I would be a richer man today.

My uncle George was rouping-out after some forty-five years in the fine farm of Benshie near Kirriemuir. The Howe of Strathmore is of course the sort of land of which we, from the plain stones of Aberdeenshire, can only dream, so I felt I was in important company at the roup on that fine sunny September day. When my uncle told me he had got £10,000 more than he expected from his roup it made me swell with pride at my part in that success. I had bought thirteen steers and been under-bidder for several more.

But I wasn't half as proud of my contribution as I would have been had I known then how those purchases would work out. They cost £534 and they sold for £563 They had eaten £34 worth of barley, £7.50 worth of silage and a whole lot of worthless wheat straw. So all I had for my labour was the muck.

Of course it could come all right yet... I still have the Ayrshire stot who has grown so tall we call him Lofty. Although he could be as much as 580 kilos now that would be asking a lot of him.

So am I to go ahead and join in this year's Spring madness? Last year's experience is hardly encouraging. But then if we paid any heed to the figures we'd all have given up years ago.

Riled by first name planners

I am becoming increasingly worried by the fact that despite my good intentions I am still not doing any of those things that it is socially acceptable for a farmer to do these days. I have hardly planted a tree, I haven't set anything aside, I have no conservation area, I haven't diversified, and even my plans for a string of duck ponds across my land have foundered at the stage of filling up the grant applications.

No, I'm afraid I'm still just producing beef and cereals and oilseeds in the seemingly vain hope that people with money will one day be short of food again. It's a gamble I feel quite justified in taking but it does leave me a bit out of things when my more conscientious friends go on about their latest projects. I really must do something.

In fact I did make a sort of a start the other day by attending a public meeting on Alternative Approaches to Country-side Conservation. The invitation came from the local chapter of the Royal Town Planning Institute and my first thought was that they should have perfected their skills in planning towns before having a go at the country.

I suppose it is a sign that I am no longer young that I am so intolerant but my suspicion of the planners was heightened when it became clear that they didn't realise that calling one and other by their first names would make the strangers in their audience feel like outsiders. "Charles" started the thing off and was hotly followed by "Willie" who really set farmer Allan's teeth on edge.

He was talking about conservation and countryside management and there he saw there being four objectives. They were: safeguarding habitats, compatible land management, private enjoyment of the countryside, and creating habitats. But where did food production come in? As they wouldn't know to call me "Charlie" I didn't get my question asked and I have no doubt it would have been hidden in there somewhere (perhaps the "habitat" that is to be preserved will include a place for me?), but really those confident and jolly young men go too far.

I was far more impressed with "Andrew" a guest speaker from the Scottish Landowner's Federation. Andrew Bradford is landed gentry and yet he turned on his hosts as no well-mannered guest should.

His thesis was that conservation wasn't only about animals and plants but also about buildings and in that last the performance of the planners was quite lamentable. He asked his hosts to consider the conundrum that has puzzled us all. How could they involve us in so much time-consuming control and still produce a countryside so inundated with alien styles and materials? How could it be that most of our pleasing buildings were built before the days of planners?

Mr. Bradford's three thousand acre estate in Deeside was, until the war, his family's holiday lodge but he is making it his home and his life's work. He has shooting, fishing, forestry, farming and property on

74

the estate and he welcomes orienteers, walkers and canoers but is fed up with dumpers, vandals and litterers. He gets the local primary school to come and plant trees and come back to see if they are growing. And they plant mixed woodlands because that is what the laird wants.

And all this without the help of planners. He does have a Site of Special Scientific Interest. They want him to cut the grass once a year in the meadow by the river. But then he always did that anyway for the convenience of the fishers.

Mr. Bradford's tour de force ended with a challenge to the bright young planners to explain why the countryside was filling up with kit houses and flat-roofed extensions underneath satellite dishes when they were taking so much of our time and our money supposedly to plan the countryside. Up to the point at which I left feeling tired no one had taken up the challenge... not even Charles or Willie.

Luckily I did stay long enough to hear what excellent value we farmers are getting from the Farm and Forestry and Wildlife Advisory Group. Their representative was introduced as "Alison".

Miss Espie, like Mr. Bradford was "no feart" and told the meeting that farmers had had too much stick over the questions of wildlife. She found that in her work she often had to tell farmers that they were trying to do more than they could afford. Farmers now needed incentives towards conservation. Her main suggestion was a Scottish version of the Countryside Premium Scheme which is in action in seven counties of England.

The idea is that, instead of just giving farmers money to grow weeds, there should be top-up payments to do something positive with the setaside land. Those lucky English farmers can get £120 a hectare extra if they sow native meadow grasses in their setaside. And if they put down a clover and Timothy mixture instead of the weeds and so help to get the wild geese through the winter, they can have £90 a hectare... and the thanks of their neighbours.

I could go for a setaside scheme along those lines.

Mossie's infernal banger

THE HARBINGERS of Spring crowd in. Golden days are almost here. Even the thrawnest of our grass has turned green now and if it wasn't for wanting to eat up the last 100 big bales of silage and as much as possible of our huge store of straw we would have all the cattle outside. We've put the few pure Simmentals out but that's mainly because they seemed to be taking turns of guarding the trough to make sure that the Jerseys didn't get more than they thought proper.

The daffodils are out and so are the flowering currant, the rhododendron and a beautiful white blossomed plant which has appeared among the willows on the steep brae that leads down to the village.

The pigeon war is won for another season. The rape is 18 inches tall and they don't like landing in stuff that is too deep for them to watch for the approach of the hunter. Of course everyone isn't as far on as we

are. Big Hamish, who was too busy driving his expensive tractors around to do anything about the cushets, has still got the sort of field the pigeons feel safe in. In fact there is so little greenery in that field that we suspect that the doos just go there for a safe roost.

Nevertheless, in a touching show of blind faith, our man has put on the fertiliser, and is now setting about shutting the stable door. He has filled up the empty brown field with tractors with the radios on, and he's even got a shot of Mossie's triple banger.

That's not a car, you understand, but an even more infernal one of those cannons which go off every few minutes to scare the birds. This one's speciality is going off a second time just as the invaders are settling down again and then making sure they leave with a third salvo. Mossie swears by the triple effect but he can spare Hamish a loan as he says his crop is so far on that it might scare away the bees which are so important for the pollination.

The larks are filling the skies again but I'm missing one of my favourite Spring cries. The lapwings (we call them Peesie-weeps) are back but they won't be nesting at Little Ardo this year. They like to get a nest in the fresh made land and I took advantage of the fine back end to do all my sowing then.

Indeed because I have no Spring sowing to do I've had enough time to go on a Department of Agriculture tour to Northern Ireland.

They were anxious, among other things, to show us what a lot they were doing to improve food hygiene, and I was very impressed. The poor old salmonellae and listeriae just don't have a chance in those modern plants.

Take the Milk Marketing Board's processing plant at Cookstown. Their ultra-heat treatment plant there is like an intensive care unit.

The milk is heated to 140 degrees centigrade... way above boiling point and then cooled rapidly to kill all the bugs. The air in the place is filtered to prevent contamination and it is quickly sealed in sterile air packs. There are only two production workers at a time in the three million pound development and the hygiene imposed on them is strict. We visitors saw the extent of that, for before we were allowed in, we had to wash with disinfective soap, cover all clothing and wear a hat. We had to be fairly agile too. for we had to put one foot up on a barrier, slip on a disposable plastic slipper, put that foot down on the other side and then put a slipper on the other foot. Several of our party found they had landed on the wrong side of the barrier and had to go through the balancing act again.

They don't even trust the the board's own tankers to approach the factory hygienically. The milk arrives by pipeline from a nearby plant.

It is quite clear that this is the sort of thing the industry has to do if we are to be seen to "put our house in order". I applaud the effort and know it will stand us in great stead for 1992 and all that, but there are dangers too. If people are to be protected from all the bugs which were once ingested without question, will we have any resistance to disease when there is a breakdown or when we go abroad or when we eat imported foods?

I have no doubt that part of the problem of food safety is caused by the rising standard of hygiene. If we eat only what is sterile how will we build up our resistance?

Here at Little Ardo we used to raise some three hundred calves a year for feeding into a barley beef unit. From time to time those calves suffered from salmonella and it wasn't uncommon for us to have a dozen scouring at once and they were treated by myself and the three men I had then.

We had to inject them and pour saline solutions down their throats and yet we took no precautions for our own health. Two of the men smoked and their hands were never far from their mouths and the best our hands would have got before eating our "piece" would have been a dicht on our trousers. And yet we never suffered salmonellosis.

I'm not suggesting that everyone should live in insanitary conditions to build up their resistance to the nasties but I do fear that the cleaner we get the worse the public health breakdowns are likely to become.

Standing where my ancestors stood; among the stones

I'VE BEEN reading that farmers in Inverness-shire and right down the West of the country have been held up by the floods. Of course I have no desire for obstruction but we are quite parched here in the North-East corner. We've been half joking for a year now about becoming semi-desert but, with last week's blocking of Morayshire roads by the topsoil, the joke is getting less funny. We expected the snowploughs to be out in March but not for that.

I told a farmer from Ayrshire the other day that our water table was supposed by some to be down ten feet. He replied that his water table was now about six feet above the ground and that the Spring work was a bit of a guddle.

No such problem here, but we are beginning to slip behind with the crop spraying because of the almost continuous wind.

There is however one job for which there is no excuse for delay. And this week I was at it. I had a couple of days getting the last of the stones off.

Of course, when I say "the last of the stones" I am not kidding myself that I have now got stone-free fields. What I mean is that I have got the last that I intend to remove this year.

I am very glad to have the job done for when He distributed His stones on the face of the earth he gave us at least our fare share, and He left them disappointingly near the surface. When we make a field for corn the prevailing impression is not so much one of brown loam but of stones. They don't seem to do the plants much harm but they play hell with the machinery. So it's part of the Spring ritual to set out with the tractor and sideless bogie to "tak aff stanes".

79

I remember forty years ago being one of a squad of five working my father's ground and that it was a rather jolly task with plenty of time between loads for the crack which used to lighten the burdens of agricultural work. It was a bit like hoeing turnips, where, with the foreman setting the pace, the tractormen following by rank and the grieve at the back where he could assess the quality of the work and make sure no one fell behind, the country's old legends and new gossip were aired endlessly.

But in these days when there isn't a squad to put out on many farms hoeing is a mighty tedious job. There can be fewer prospects more like a life sentence than starting with a hoe in a twenty-acre park and, though it is still the best husbandry, that's why the hoeing has all but died out.

Well now, "takin' aff stanes" is a bit like the hoeing. You crawl across the field with very little to show for your work, and if you do it alone as I do you have to drag the arthritic knees in and out and in and out of the tractor-cab without the respite of any cheery word.

And yet I have to say that I like taking off the stones. It has

something to do with standing where my ancestors have stood. The fact that there are only as many stones on Little Ardo as there are is a testament to their toil. The stone dykes, the neat piles built on the roadsides which were thought useless for anything else, are incidental monuments to five generations of us.

Of course the fertility of the soil which they found as rocky hillside and peat moss and can now grow three and a half tonnes of grain, is also a monument to their good husbandry. The carefully worked rotation which added muck, and the seaweed and guano all contributed and yet, when I put muck on my fields I don't get the same communion with the Mackies and the Yulls.

They put out muck with the graip and the barrow to the midden, then they used the graip to fill the little horse carts. In the fields they used the clique to pull the muck off the carts in great dollops... about a barrowful at a time. And finally they spread the heaps again by hand graip. It was back-breaking work that tore the skin off the toughest hands.

I just use the digger to fill the mucking cart straight from the courts and drive round the

80

field like a gentleman. And the same is true of nearly everything about the farm. The modern way is so mechanised as to be quite unlike what the old-timers did.

It is only when I'm gathering stones that I can look my forebears in the eye and say "I am truly following in your footsteps". In fact, if my great-grandfather ever took off stones on his own, he will have had it easier than me. It is true that he had to tip his load by getting his shoulder under the shaft and lifting, whereas I have a hydraulic ram under my cart, but, where I have to heave myself in and out of the tractor at every shift, all he would have had to do was to make that curious kissing noise that horsemen used to make and the horsie would move off by herself.

When I take off a stone I feel it is a contribution to the place. Although it is true that next year the plough will find another stone, at least none of my progeny will ever have to "tak aff' that particular stone again.

There isn't much farm work about which you can say "that won't have to be done again".

There's no old men to talk to, and no youngsters to impress

IN THE Winters long ago, when we ploughed with one or two furrow ploughs, and when there was no automatic reset, and when tyres had to last to the canvas and there was no power steering, we seemed to spend the whole dark days of Winter blackening the ground. There were tatties to dress and beasts to be kept in an endless supply of neeps and silage but the main task of Winter, for the outside squad, was ploughing.

Of course, even in those harder times and before the quiet safety cabs, there were days when even the hardest grieve gave up and let us all stay inside. The fire was put on in the tractor shed and all the old stories were given an airing along with whoever in the village had been caught doing any of those things the doing of which is better kept dark.

They were delicious days of stolen leisure. Not that we were quite idle. There were always balls of binder twine to be rolled up, the nets that covered the stacks of unthreshed grain or potato baskets to be mended. But that was the sort of work that left a man fresh at the end of the day and put a boy in touch with his heritage.

I had such a day recently. Or it would have been for it was foul enough to justify putting on the tractor shed fire. But there would have been no point. There are no longer old men to talk to on the farm or youngsters to impress.

On the other hand there is no one to whom I have to account so I just stayed in the house and took up sociology. I know of no better definition of that science than the following; "Sociology is what sociologists do", and I

hear there are a large number doing it these days so why not me?

All day I worked on my analysis which provides an entirely new system for classifying farmers. Usually it is; dairy farmer, arable farmer, fish farmer and so on. John Ross is a hill farmer and Maitland Mackie is an agri-businessman. But that is pretty unhelpful as the agri-businessman is also a dairy farmer and an arable farmer all at the same time.

My new classification is based on the kinds of wives farmers have, and that has the advantage of meaning that, unless they have more than one wife, they must be in one category only.

Class one farmers, then, are those whose wives, as well as keeping the house and shouting at the children, have to run an enterprise on the farm. They'll rear calves or feed hens. They'll act as a gate when there are stots to be wormed and the best of them will push a barrowful of silage.

In Class Two the wife goes out to work, often as a schoolteacher. This most common form of diversification leads to the employment of someone else to do the housework.

Then there's the Class Three farmer. His wife's function is largely decorative and reproductive. But she is also a manager. She organises the household, takes phone messages, co-ordinates the farmer's social life and makes sure that the children have a new pair of sensible shoes before they go off to their boarding schools. That hardly gives the class three wives a full-time job so they are available for coffee mornings, curling and good work.

Me now, I'm a second class farmer.

Fiona goes off to the city to work as a computorer and hires Gladys to look after me and answer the phone.

The great changes that have been wreaked on our industry in recent years have been reflected in the class structure in my new classification. Just as many gentleman farmers have had to put on their boots to help cope with the deterioration in profitability, so many farmers have found themselves moving up from class three to class two as they find it necessary to put the wife out to work.

Then again, with the change in attitudes to women's role in society, many of the "gates" have emancipated themselves by finding a job and so moved their husbands into class two. In fact the recent social history of Scottish agriculture shows a convergence on class two.

Mind you there are exceptions. I was nearly moved from class two into class one recently.

My wife was between jobs and, despite all the evidence to the contrary, decided she wouldn't manage to get another job. She threatened to stay at home. She would keep hens and grow mushrooms and she would milk a cow. We even had the milking machine bought.

Now I love her dearly but this was a horrendous prospect. I have got used to having the house to myself in the middle of the day. I can come in for my dinner when I please. I then put on the fire and settle down uninterrupted to watch Business Daily on the tele. On good days I don't wake up till Neighbours comes on. If the wife were at home all that would go... and there would certainly be no time for sociology.

She has got a new job though. I'm so happy for her... and my place in class two is assured.

April 23, 1990

Wrong attitude to whisky

AS I was telling you last week, I am a class two farmer, having a wife who goes out to work. Fiona works as a systems analyst which means she knows more about computers than would be good for the likes of me.

When she gets home she cooks an excellent supper and then has a while at the garden before getting on with her hobby. That is going down to the wood and dragging home timber which she saws up to keep our home fires burning brightly. As she is also putting some of her earnings away in case we have an old age and as she decorates the interior of our rambling and crumbling old farmhouse, you can see that I am not doing too badly in the wife department.

However I must tell you today that this paragon does have a fault with which I have in the past found it hard to live. It lies in her attitude to strong drink in general and whisky in

particular.

She thinks whisky is mainly for creating a strong market for malting barley. Otherwise it is for keeping in the cupboard in case visitors come, one of us has a feverish cold or someone falls in the river and needs reviving.

None of those events comes nearly often enough for me and I take an entirely different approach. I believe that whisky is one of God's finest gifts and a suitable reward for any good day's labour. It soothes the aching limbs and stimulates the tired brain to artful conversation.

Fiona's views and mine were quite clearly irreconcilable and in fact it is many years now since we reached a compromise. Since then, I have been allowed one dram per night (but one dram only) and peace to drink it, free from reminders about the wages of sin.

A body has to work within the rules, so that very Christ-

85

mas I bought the wife a pair of the most beautiful and enormous crystal tumblers you ever saw.

When I am pouring my nightly dram I play my trump card. That is my known particularity about how much water to add. I pour myself a modest dram and add water and taste. Sadly I observe that I have drowned it and take the only reasonable course by adding more whisky. Again I overdo it and have to add a little more water. And you know, try as I may, I never seem to get the mixture quite right until my great crystal trough is brimming full.

So, you see, despite only having one dram per night, I have a considerable stake in the consumption end of the whisky business and am duly disgusted by the Chancellor's so-called neutral budget... fifty pence a bottle is surely too much just when the malting trade seemed to be getting to it's feet.

The production side doesn't affect me this year as I sowed all my barley in the back-end and won't have any suitable for malting. And there is some respite also on the consumption side; the local shop has announced that they won't put on the fifty pence as long as stocks last. That won't be long the way things are going.

What has been holding me up is wondering if I could get a few bottles past my accountant on the grounds that my nightly tipple is a management tool... certainly most of my decisions are made with it's aid.

And there are plenty of precedents. My father and the generations before him used to go down to the shop and ask for nails. That was the signal to be shown into the backshop where there were other farmers and smoke and general conviviality. My father never seemed to bring any nails home from those sessions but he must have got them for, at the term time, the half yearly account itemised so many consignments you'd have thought we were running a joiner's business at Little Ardo.

And of course we used to use whisky as a drug for ailing cattle.

It was long after ten o'clock and his bedtime when Pat Joss, who used to sleep above the shop, was wakened by a banging at the door. It was Geordie Gill, the grieve at Little Ardo, wanting a pint of whisky for a sick stirkie.

With an ill grace Pat Joss came down the stairs. In an

agricultural community in those days everyone realised that the demands of the beasts must come first but they didn't have to like it. Pat was in a foul mood as he thrust the half bottle out of the door.

He grumbled his way upstairs bewailing to himself his five o'clock start the next morning. As he was blowing out the light he thought he heard the "plop" of a cork coming out of a bottle. There followed some gurgling noises below his window, followed by a delicious long sigh of satisfaction.

Then he heard a chuckle and the unmistakable voice of Geordie Gill saying, "Aye, the stirkie's feelin' better already".

Flirting with the goodlife

I AM relieved to announce that I have finally done one of those OK, trendy, green things. No, still no duckpond or good land laid down to trees, but I have taken a bit out of production. That will reduce my use of harmful nitrogen and reduce my ability to produce costly surpluses for the European taxpayer to buy.

When my parents farmed this place they had a large kitchen garden which kept us in potatoes, lettuces, Brussels sprouts, leeks and carrots for the soup and peas for me to guzzle straight from the pod.

Unfortunately, when Fiona and I took over, we were too busy to grow vegetables. A run-down farm, a huge overdraft, a school-teaching job and four querulous children were enough without growing our own vegetables. I grew sixteen acres of potatoes in the fields so there seemed very little point in a few more in the garden.

At any rate, about 1975 we put the kitchen garden down to lawn and some fruit trees, canes, bushes and plants.

And yet this week, some fifteen years later we opened our new kitchen garden. It is our extensification, diversification, our flirtation with "the good-life", and my wife even talks about our new garden going organic.

The decision had something to do with Willie. He's our once-a-week gardener who has made such a success of tidying us up. The place looks good now but there isn't much in the way of a crop to show for his wages. Now what a pensioner gets for working in a garden isn't much, but the hard times in farming have made us look always for a return. So we must have our vegetables from the garden.

It was decided to plough and fence a bit of the old ley in front of the house. But that isn't the sort of job about which it is easy to get a contractor excited so the ploughing was never getting done. So why didn't I plough it myself?

Well you see my early farming life was dominated by the great James Low who was grieve at Little Ardo for 44 years. He had learned to plough with the horse during the first world war when so many men were away that he got a pair when he was only fifteen. It must have been a hard apprenticeship for the boy but it certainly made him a good ploughman and a hard man.

In fact James Low believed that it was impossible to understand the plough unless you spent several years following a pair of Clydesdales. No one who "wanted to have a go" or was "willing to learn" had any hope. To be a ploughman you had to be forced there by poverty and held there by terror.

That somewhat discouraging philosophy meant that I never even learned to plough average-to-badly.

Nevertheless, embarrassed by the approach of Spring and deaved by my wife's complaints, I eventually took the 590 and nipped over to our contractor for a shot of his three furrow, reversible plough... that would soon tame our tenth of an acre vegetable patch.

I was mildly embarrassed that I needed a hand to get the plough on and mortified when I failed to lift it. The trouble... a broken compression spring on the three point linkage. I slunk off home.

It was almost as bad as my first ever bash at the ploughing many years ago.

The ploughman had gone off with the wheat field half done and left the plough on the old 5000. I was emboldened by an aristocratic friend who started ploughing a few days after seeing his first farm. "Oh it's easy," he'd said, " I just follow the other chap round".

Admittedly the other chap wasn't there to follow but I had no difficulty seeing where he had been. I'd do a couple of acres and then maybe in the evening I'd go down to the village and get one of the old ploughman to give me the "Horsemen's grip and word"... the secrets necessary for entry into the Society of Ploughmen.

There was to be no such success. My first attempt at the plough was slapstick of a high order.

As I remember it, and I do not remember it clearly, I set out at a leisurely pace but ground to a halt after about ten paces. "Not enough revs", I thought, and opened her up. Off I set but the wheels began to rise. "Too far in," I thought and hauled the lift handle. This made the tractor rear up and swing drunkenly to the left. I pulled right but the plough was in control. I banged the side brake. This brought my bucking bronco swinging round and I careered out of the drill and did wheelies all over Gordon's good ploughing. When the plough fell off I went home in disgust. Entry into the Society of Ploughmen would have to wait.

I was so glad that the old grieve wasn't there to enjoy my discomfort and all the ploughman would say on Monday was "Aye Charlie. You must have had a fair weekend."

It was a sympathetic reaction for which I have always thought kindly of Gordon. And I must report another such. After my humiliation with the reversible falling off on Monday the contractor arrived on Tuesday with his own tractor and had the kitchen garden beautifully ploughed in about five minutes.

90

Village gossips way out

LITTLE ARDO'S been a well known farm for a hundred and fifty years. It has been farmed in turn by the Royal Highland and Agricultural Society medal winner for reclamation William Yull and by his son John, the famous auctioneer. His grand-daughter's husband and president of the National Farmer's Union, Maitland Mackie was next, followed by his son-in-law, the writer John R. Allan and I, of course, have kept the old place in the news.

But now the farm on the "Little Hill" has a quite new and altogether more spectacular claim to notoriety thanks to the next generation. It was the scene of an event which threatens to be sung forever where the people of Methlick foregather to discuss the misfortunes of others.

We had taken advantage of a visit from our son Jay to have a few days away from the cows and telephone. And he took advantage of our absence to hold the very mother and father of a party.

It is fine to live on top of the little hill and look down on the picturesque village below. But it does mean that if you are going to have a party with reinforced concrete music, and if the party is to last until eight o'clock in the morning, there's not much chance of anyone in the village overlooking the fact. Indeed if everyone was telling the truth few even slept.

Certainly they could speak of little else... even the readers of the *Sun* broke off from speculating about whether there had been thirty deaths at Strangeways or more. "There had been traffic jams in Methlick at two-thirty am. Boghead had phoned the police because he was up all night at the lambing and couldn't hear himself think. The music had been so loud the ornaments on Peenie Wallace's mantle-piece had been rocking. Charlie Allan's house had been wrecked and they'd even broken the leg of the grand piano with dancing on top of that. They'd been running buses from the more disreputable dives in Aberdeen. The police had been out in force and arrested half of them. When the dawn sunlight glinted on the windows of the

the shafts, and no collar… just the old man holding onto her tail. Yes, great grandfather, a renowned reveller and poacher, would have been proud to be there.

But it did upset the neighbours. The farmer of Gowkstone, for example, he got a

house there were even those in the village who swore it was flames licking the curtains."

As I write, a draft sweeps my face though there is not an open door or window in the house. Without doubt I have disturbed the ghost of John Yull who would have loved to be at young Jay's do. John it was who won a bet when, in drink, he drove his gig home from Maud market, all eight miles of the way, with his great mare Clatterin' Jean between

terrible fright. He had had been wetting a baby's head on the night of the party and had gone to bed very late and considerably the better of drink. The benefits however had worn off and Gowkie was paying the price when, at eight o'clock the next morning he was piloting his car shakily along the old rough road that separates his farm from mine. Suddenly, and for the first recorded time, he met a police car on that nonroad. His heart sank. If they even asked him anything he would be sunk. But no. Still, he had almost swallowed his false teeth.

It really is amazing how the concern for the welfare of the rest of the countryside will make us blow up the small events of our lives. Perhaps too many of us have been reading the *Sun* and have become even greedier for sensation.

When we came home we found everything in order. The party hadn't been held in the house and in a clever move to foil the wagging tongues Jay had left the key in the safe-keeping of Gladys our cleaning lady. The old tattie shed was the disco and the only thing I could see that wasn't as I left it was that they hadn't managed to put all the dirt, broken tattie boxes and abandoned wheels back in the shed.

There had been no arrests. The five police cars had just been keeping a precautionary eye on things and they were most welcome. As well as adding to the speak of the village they were a great help to the farmers. As Mossie put it "A' that police cars fleein' roon the countryside in the early mornin' fairly kept the doos aff the rape".

The ultimate deception goes wrong by multiples

I'VE BEEN forced into a U-turn in the management of my Jersey hill cows.

You will recall that the scheme was to transplant pure beef embryos into the Channel Islanders. They would be easy calvers, frugal eaters and be great milkers which would enable me to put an extra calf onto each. As I can get the hill cow subsidy I would be able to rear myself some beef calves for little or nothing.

Well, we've got off to a start. The calves are lively and so far eighty per-cent bulls. They are small though and I'll reserve judgment on their conformation but in the matter of calving they have been no bother at all.

I told you about the little squint-nosed heifer we called Lottie (after Toulouse Lautrec) and how she was given two cross Limousin calves in January. Well that is going really well. They're outside now and all are healthy and seem happy. The calves are at least two hundredweight each, but even here there is a snag.

While the calves grow daily bigger Lottie seems to grow daily smaller. She is fit and well and the picture of motherhood but in her efforts to do her best for her brood she is now well below the five hundredweight she was when she got the calves. At this rate the day can't be far off when all three of them may all be the same size... perhaps 200 kilos. Now the question is "Are we going to be able to get her back in calf?"

Local Jersey breeders have warned me that that is likely to be a problem. But that isn't really what has caused me to have a bit of a rethink on my system.

You see it is all very well when you have the odd cow

calving to decide to give her an extra calf to help her pay her bills. A quick phone call to the local milk producers will produce a calf the same day and with only one adoption to supervise at a time the whole thing seems worth it. But what I am faced with at the moment is a calving season and that is an altogether different proposition.

It's everybody else's calving season as well so that by the time you get your turn of a dairy calf your cow has become quite used to feeding only one and adoption becomes a long and tedious process. It's made much the worse for the fact that there are many more potential adoptions than there are pens to hold them and by the certain knowledge that they should all be outside by now anyway.

To solve the availability problem I bought a batch of Simmental cross Friesian bull calves from Somerset. A major investment surely at £265 per head, though that was £30 less than last year. As soon as a cow was clear of her own calf I would be ready with her extra one.

But the Jersey cows still seemed to be fit for me.

I decided to go all out for the ultimate in deception.

The next cow to calve was seen as her waters broke. I rushed with my bucket and scooped up all I could. By the time she calved three hours later I had half a calf's pailful of somewhat unappetising slime.

I then selected a Somerset calf, tied his legs together so that he couldn't get up, placed him along with the newly born calf at the rear of the cow and rubbed my bucketful well in. I then untied the cow who rose to find not one but two calves as the reward of her labour.

The deception was a complete success. She set about licking them both until the were clean if not dry.

I was elated. What a triumph. It just showed you that if you plan the thing properly and do everything just right, almost anything can be achieved in animal husbandry.

True in general perhaps, but not this time. My carefully laid scheme went agley because, of all things, though the cow was quite happy to have him, and indeed showed him affection, the calf hadn't the slightest inclination to suck... he was still baaing for his milk pail a day later and a day after that he got it.

That was the day I discovered that the best calf on the

place, a brosy Charolais, had decided to wean himself though he was only three months old and that a big Aberdeen-Angus calf who had a cow all to himself had decided he preferred to share what poor Lottie had to offer. It was that day that I went off multiple suckling.

Sandy of the fertile family

"HOW DID you get on sellin' your stores then Andra?"

"Oh grand. Aye, great trade."

"That's good, so you'd got what you expected then?"

"Oh no, but I didna expect to get aa' that", said Andra.

I tell you that story mainly because it is one of my favourites. It says so much about the farmers' peculiar combination of optimism and realism. And the ability to laugh at ourselves which helps to substitute for a realistic return on capital.

I am reminded of it because I am missing going to the store sales this spring. It is, after all, at the ringsides that all the old stories are retold and there's always the chance of hearing a new one. I seem to hear a higher percentage of new ones these days but I suspect it's just that as time goes on I forget more and more of the old ones.

Though I dearly love to go to the sales, and especially to join in the spring madness, I have found it just too difficult to get away this year. That's the trouble with being a one man band on the place. With 120 cattle to receive varying amounts of attention, including calves to be fed and foster mothers to be cajoled each day, as well as 170 acres of crops to be admired, it's hard to get away. I find a week in Greece is O.K. – then someone has to be fee-ed, but half a day at Maud or at Thainstone seems almost impossible.

However I have been represented. And by an agent with the highest possible pedigree. My friend Sandy is a Fowlie. He is one of that fertile family whose domination of the cattle finishing trade in the North East is well into the third generation. It would be nothing to have two Sandy Fowlies, two John Fowlies and two James Fowlies round the ring at once and for the family still to be represented at all the other major centres in a 100 miles radius.

Now my man is a Sandy of the third generation. He came by wisdom, in equal measure, but later than is usual in that gifted family. That means that fewer than four hundred cattle fills him up in the spring time so that he has time to buy a few for his friend Charlie.

A modest commission is of course involved but it seems to me that, as that has to be paid for out of the difference between Sandy's skill as a buyer and mine, it represents outstanding value.

My man gives a score out of only three in the store rings. Three is "good cattle". Two is "decent stirks". And one is "plain brutes". Sandy has managed to get me filled up with cattle scoring two on that scale at about 112 pence a kilo. That is well below the quoted averages, makes me optimistic of a good return, and is far in advance of the sort of success I would have expected to achieve myself.

Mind you, even I can have my moments. Do you remember my telling you about Lofty the tall, thin Ayrshire steer I bought last spring for a pound a kilo. He was a quite outstanding example of the "plain brute" class of cattle and did the farm no credit beside the main Methlick to Fyvie road all summer. We bought him some pals in the backend and they shared a trough till the turn of the year when they all went fat and left Lofty to grow taller yet.

We finally got fed up of him in early March. He went to Thainstone where he made a price almost ten pence below the quoted minimum for the day. And yet, with the subsidy, that came to some 94 pence a kilo. That was 6 pence less than we'd paid but he'd grown from a plain brute of 350 kilos to a big plain brute of 640 kilos. I had over two hundred and fifty pounds to pay for 10 months corn so I don't feel that Lofty died in my debt.

It is odd how there can be bargains even in the most enthusiastic markets. And my buyer thinks he has sent me the snip of this spring. He's a 334 kilo Red Hereford steer which cost £332. How it could be I don't know for this is a class two – a decent stirk – the sort of thing that, being what they call a handy weight, has been making 130 pence regularly and 150 pence when the spring madness has been at it's height.

I'll let you know how he works out.

In the meantime Sandy's

success as a buyer is a bit demeaning as far as I'm concerned. It means I now have a crops consultant to tell me how to grow my cereals, I have the man from Financial Control Services to make sure I'm not going broke, I have contractors to do everything that needs a machine costing more than £3,000 and now Sandy to do my cattle buying. So what sort of a farmer am I?

Well, there are all those courts to be mucked out.

Oilseed rape is the star turn

A FORTNIGHT ago the only thing that appeared to stand between us and a second consecutive profitable year (would that be a record?) was the drought. We'd had hardly a drop of rain all spring and nothing to gladden the heart all winter. The spring barley was desperately dry. That didn't affect me as I have only winter cereals but even they were beginning to show signs of stress.

Everything was looking well but the danger signs were there.

And then, quite suddenly, and without much warning from the weather-men, it started to rain early one evening. It was a little rain at first... not much more than the haar we expect off the summer seas. But gradually it built up.

We had a small libation to celebrate the laying of the dust after half an hour of it. Half way down the dram I couldn't resist nipping out to see if it was off yet. No, it was raining a little harder. Back inside I went with the good news and finished the dram. When I looked out fifteen minutes later it had got heavier and, despite our rule that I am only allowed one dram per night, I was conceded another. After-all, the night the drought breaks is no ordinary night.

There were many other happy visits to the door, many reports of further good news, and several more relaxations of discipline. Three hours it rained and farmer and his wife went very happily to bed that night. In the morning there was what an optimist could call half an inch in the water gauge.

And what a difference it made. We've now had a fortnight of intermittent rain and everything has just jumped. The winter barley, which had been short enough for Baldie to forecast a "year of the short corn", and which started to shoot on the first of May, sprung up six inches and still wasn't full shot a fortnight later. The wheat had seemed very slow. The main spring dressing had been lying on the top for days waiting for water and evaporating quietly into the ozone layer. It has jumped too, though perhaps not as much as the barley, and it has at last taken on that rich deep green that promises a bounteous harvest.

But the star turn is the oil seed rape. Although in full flower when the rain came, it has grown about an inch a day since. The Tapidor is now four foot six high with a yellow head on it two feet deep while the Cobra is a good foot higher though the flowers may not be quite so dense. And the price has been rising too. It looks quite possible that we might be able to beat last year's mouth-watering £300 a tonne.

My optimism was overflowing when I went to the discussion group on Sunday. I let it go into the second pint before telling Mossie, with all the restraint at my command, that my Cobra was up to six foot four tall. Now Mossie, who has the reputation of being able to grow combinable crops on a tarmac road, was certainly the man to blaw to if I wanted taking down off my high.

"What a disaster," he said.

That was not the reaction for

which I had hoped.

"No, no. I've told you before. All show no dough. That great high stuff'll just go as flat as a bannock in the first plump of rain about Highland Show time. Then the seeds'll rot and what doesn'a rot'll sprout. You won't be able to get the swather under it so it'll have to be cut direct and that'll shake off any berries that remain. Disaster. Jist a disaster."

Not known for his concern for the feelings of his fellow farmers, even Mossie could see that his advice hadn't brightened my day. "Mind you", he said, "it could be all right. If there's no rain between now and harvest time and if there's no wind to shake it out in August you could get half a crop, and that's about all you're used to anyway."

It was all very depressing. What am I supposed to do? Do I have to grow poor little crops that can hide from the wind and can stand the rain? Should I have let the pigeons eat it all through the winter? No one was denying that Big Hamish's rape would stand as it was barely a foot high yet.

It got me to thinking about how things have become and how they have not improved. With this breatheliser I couldn't even have another drink to sharpen my wits for a reply to the great cerealiser. Now that's something that wouldn't have worried my great grandfather John Yull.

In the course of his duties as an auctioneer he did a considerable amount of business dramming and after that was done he never denied himself a few more. But he didn't have to drive home for he went everywhere by gig. And when the party was over he would climb aboard, with varying degrees of help from his friends. He would fall asleep immediately and, as the cool night air cleared his tired brain, his trustie mare would take him home.

Her name was Clatterin' Jean and as long as the event had been in Aberdeenshire she would take John Yull home unguided. When old Mrs. Yull heard the horse nudging at the stable door she would rise, take the old man in to his bed and stable the horse.

What a horse...and what a wife!

June 4, 1990

Planted firs round the piggery

IT WAS at the tail end of the war that my mother and I toiled up the bumpy brae for the first time. We had come by bus and we had come in a spirit of high adventure for Little Ardo was to be our new home and our own farm.

There were only my mother and I, as my poor father was still required to put the finishing touches to Hitler and Hirohito. He had been an unlikely hero. A gentle man, who had made his progress by wit rather than force, he had nevertheless risen from Sapper to Captain by the time he was demobbed in 1945. "A good war" you might think. But, when he was asked what sort of a war he had had, my father replied, "Long".

At any rate his reward was to be the chance to buy his mother-in-law's family farm for just over £4,000... the same price that the Laird had asked when he sold it in 1920. My mother and I were the advance guard as we arrived at Little Ardo to claim our inheritance.

I was not favourably impressed.

It was a cold and wet winter's day. The house had been empty for years and echoed as we trudged around the wooden floors and my mother tried to be cheery about who would sleep where and which would be the sitting room.

But it wasn't the inside of the house that disappointed me. It was the bareness of the place. The only cover was a very few very large elm, plain and ash trees and quite the most miserable, thin hawthorn hedge which, had it been thicker, might have helped separate the house from the steading. It was that hedge that best defined my disappointment with Little Ardo.

You see, the war effort had claimed both of my parents and I spent much of the time with my grandparents at Tarves. That was not a sacrifice for North Ythsie was a heavenly

103

place. The house there stood in an acre of it's own ground with carefully shaped and manicured lawns. The kitchen garden was about half an acre and produced more fruit than a boy could possibly eat and, much more important, it was surrounded by a tall and luxuriant hedge.

It was my eagerest anticipation in the Spring of the year to be up each morning and round that hedge, for I had a passion for birds and their nests. It was so thick that you could miss a nest in it one morning and discover it there the next. Then there were trees all round the garden and those round the kitchen garden had been cut off at about six feet which let the rot in and made nesting holes for starlings and for owls.

After that Little Ardo turned out a sore disappointment.

My parents too found the place somewhat bare and when the hero returned he set about afforestation. His diaries of the time show that he spent a good deal of his time at planting round the house and steading a mixture of beeches, larch, poplar, willows and spruce… and that I "helped".

It was all very exciting, and as far as I was concerned it was all for the sake of the birds that would one day come to build their nests at Little Ardo.

We must have been well on with the planting on 12 January 1947. The old man's diary showed it was the first Sunday after Epiphany. "Planted 150 Douglas firs round the piggery.

104

Damp and a thin wind. Charles, helping, exclaimed ecstatically, 'What a bird's nests there'll be here some day'. There is no doubting his interest. Mine is just some shelter".

My grandfather used to tell of a friend of his who had spent a considerable portion of the first half of his life aching for a scout knife... one of those heavy contraptions with several blades, a corkscrew, a bottle opener and a spike for taking stones out of horses' hooves. He'd been a poor boy and could never afford one. However one day, a grown man and having done well for himself even without a scout knife, he was walking in Union Street in Aberdeen when he saw a beauty in a shop window. In great excitement he went in and fulfilled his life's ambition by buying one.

As he walked off down the street looking wonderingly at his prize it gradually dawned on him that he had absolutely no use for a scout knife. His purchase had come twenty years too late.

And something like that has happened with the birds at Little Ardo. Here I sit surrounded by my father's trees. And they're full of birds. Unfortunately I grew out of my passion for birds nesting in the 1950s.

But all is not lost. For I have grandchildren now and they are kind enough to show enthusiasm and even wonder as I show them the nests.

We have just had a magical sunny Sunday afternoon when, in the garden, I was able to show them a thrush's nest being built, a blackbird's with five eggs, a woodpigeon with two and two chaffinches' with five eggs in each. I could only point at the magpie's as it is too far up the poplar tree and I didn't like to show them the wren's nest as wrens are so easily upset and their nest was so low down that I feared the little fingers would venture back to pry.

I hope John R. Allan was looking down at me and my three little girls. His trees have made this once bare hill something of a paradise in Spring. They are a memorial of which I am sure he is proud.

Old rule is the best guide

THERE IS a school of thought which believes that, as too much is being written and said about Bovine Spongiform Encephalopathy, those of us who have the interests of beef producers at heart would do best to keep quiet and wait until, as it surely will, the storm blows bye.

Unfortunately, if I am to keep faith with this column as a diary, silence isn't really an option for me. I can't very well say "here is my diary for the week, but discretion dictates that I say nothing about what is most occupying me at the moment".

And there is nothing that has had a look in this week against BSE.

Everybody is talking about it of course. The prices of fat cattle are down about 20 pence a kilo and several of my neighbours have been holding their cattle back in the hope things will get better. They will of course, but when? And will that be before I have some fat?

I have some that are almost there now so what should I do? It is very tempting to keep them for a few weeks and, in the case of the heifers, to put them to the bull. He's going to work soon anyway and I'm sure he would welcome a few more comfortably rounded Hereford- Friesian heifers.

I have given the matter an unusual amount of thought and come to the conclusion that the old rule is the best guide. It says "The time to sell fat cattle is when they are fat".

If I bull my heifers and a thousand other farmers do the same, then we are going to produce a heap of extra beef for an uncertain market in three years time. As the only thing that ever did farmers any good was a shortage, that is hardly going to help.

And I'm not going to hold onto my fat stots either. The price is down maybe 10 pence in the store rings as well so the

right policy must be to sell at the usual time and replace them immediately with the cheaper stores. That will support the store markets, give the abbatoirs the throughput they need and, much more importantly, avoid snarling the market up with fatty beef when the day comes that they have to go.

If we hold off selling we are going to have to take a smaller price because they are over-fat and we are going to be supplying the market with more beef in the end of the day because the cattle will have more time to grow.

It may be hard to take a loss on the cattle I have on the place now, but if I keep selling as usual and replace with stores immediately then, over whatever time it takes for the prices to recover their old level, I should recoup my loss.

So I know what I should do about my cattle. But what should I do about BSE? Should I join the conspiracy of silence?

Well, I think not. That way we leave the field to the hysterics and to Mr. Gummer and I don't fancy leaving them free to attack nor him as my only defence.

The situation is ludicrous. Historians of this time will no doubt chronicle the "Age of Hypochondria Gastromania" which occurred just as the last of the British Empire was being swept away. The Salmonella and the Listereosis will have honourable mentions but BSE will surely have pride of place.

honourable mentions but BSE will surely have pride of place. That was the time the British almost gave up their traditional staple source of protein because of the disputed possibility that one day a human being might contract a disease, because a mouse which had had a transplant of infected brains had contracted the disease, and because two cats had caught something similar.

I have a friend who is so impressed by the last statistic that he has opined that the risks are now just too great. For that reason he and his family have decided that they will never eat another cat.

And perhaps rather than silence the traditional British virtue, humour, however bitter, is the way to approach the question. Certainly one of our local butchers here in Aberdeenshire is seeing the irony, though he hasn't seen any overall decline in business. When asked for a pound of mince the other day he said "Yes, now we've two types of mince today, Madam. There's the ordinary mince and the BSE mince". I am relieved to tell you that the good woman chose the BSE type without a smile.

The same butcher has also had a lady who said she was frightened of the beef this week and would just have mince. Another, instead of her usual sirloin steak, said she was just going to have a salad. She left the shop with a bit of meat loaf and some cold roast beef to go with it.

Now, as you would think we would all know, any risk there is from mince and from meat loaf, is a thousand times reduced in sirloin steak which cannot have come from the old dairy cows who have been going mad with BSE. And yet somehow, the ignorance of the consumers is so great that they can think they are protecting themselves by eating sausages rather than beef.

It is terribly unfair that we are being ripped apart by such ignorance and the only way to help is for us who know a little about it to speak up.

From bed to girse, with your back to the wall

I'm looking forward eagerly to the show this year. I always enjoy it, of course, but I've got a special reason in 1990. This year I'll be able to concentrate on the delights of the show because I won't be working.

For the last eight years I have gone to the show as a broadcaster which was great fun, of course but it was a bit wearing. While you are there or thereabouts all the time there is always the anxiety that the news is breaking somewhere else. Then, when the programme is done and whatever the mess you've made it is at least over, you rush around trying to catch up with all the conviviality you've had to refuse during the day. You don't find the people you're looking for but there are lots of others and all too soon you are waking up again, feeling not too good and worrying gently about what will go wrong with the next day's programme.

There was one year that I went to the Show as a highland games athlete. I didn't like that. The main arena at Ingliston is one of the marvels of the farming world during the grand parades of cattle. And it is just the right place for thirty heavy horse turn-outs. But it is just too big for highland games. The sheer size of the arena dwarfed our efforts and there was no crowd reaction other than polite applause at the end.

The only excitement on that occasion was when the commentator (not the highly professional regular, Jimmy Spankie) told the crowd that they would easily recognise one of our number as he had the white knees which proved he only wore the kilt once a year. Our man may have lacked a sense of humour but he resented that and had to be restrained.

But of course, by far the most of my Highland Shows have been as a different kind of competitor, or at least looking after my cows which were competitors. That is hard work indeed.

I suffered my first show under the tutelage of the late Willie Rollo, then with the Kair herds of Shorthorns and Simmentals. His excuse for getting me up at six was that I had to hurry and get the "girse". Despite having been brought up in Aberdeenshire I took a while to realise that that was grass.

You've really no idea how much girse a cow eats when she is grazing. But just try carrying her girse for her in a big square of hessian... then you know. And old Willie was no fool. He would show me how to look after my two cows and the calf, but I would in turn carry the girse for his team of Shorthorns and his team of Simmentals as well for as my own.

I soon found that my problems were only started with the getting of the grass. They seemed to digest the stuff almost immediately and indeed the green that came out seemed to be even more than that which went in...certainly it was more difficult to get rid of. And my cattle were always the dirtiest. I was forever cleaning them up. My graip and shovel were never still.

It took me several more visits to shows and sales to realise that cows need a lot of water to produce the instant digestive performance. When I had learned to keep my cattle just a wee bit short of water I had learned the way to make them look full and fat and to keep them clean.

I never doubted that I had a lot to learn but I was a bit surprised when, despite my obeying Willie's every instruction and watching his every move, my two cows were last in the cow class and the calf held up the junior heifers. On the other hand the Kair lot all got tickets including the supreme championships in both breeds.

I am sure you will be thinking that that would be because my cattle weren't good enough, but I am absolutely sure that that was no more than a small part of the trouble. You see I brought one of those two cows back to the Highland Show some six years later and carried off the championship myself.

Oh yes. There is a great deal to the showing of cattle.

There are those who will say that the art of the showman

is kidology and nothing to do with the business of breeding better stock. I disagree and will try to tell you why another time. In the meantime I'm looking forward to seeing the showman's art at it's best again this year, without having to struggle at it myself.

Like most of the other cattlemen (shepherds et all) the busy life of a showman was graced at that time by life in the most dismal of domestic circumstances. We lived in the herdsman's quarters... wooden huts who's only advantage was being near to the cattle and whose only amenity was a nail on the back of the door to hang your trousers if you ever had the time or the incentive to take them off.

The walls were that thin you could hear the man in the next hut turn over, the one next down snoring, a gentle argument over moral principles three along and the inevitable sing-song wherever in the concentration camp it occurred.

The best of those parties took place, not in the huts, but in the Austin Hotel. That was an old Austin float belonging to one of the exhibitors. It would tell a few tales if only it could.

By the time of my second show I had acquired a cattleman called Gordon and a float of my own. So, having tried the huts and found them picturesque but inadequate, we decided to live in the Gordon Arms. It was a converted furniture van. It had its own bed

111

above the cab and as the man who sold it put it "a sink and a kettle and aathing".

Unfortunately aathing didn't include much ventilation and we had been too busy to clean her out properly after the journey. It had been a roasting hot day which had matured the dung more than somewhat, and the stink was quite unbearable. In ten minutes I had the sleeping bag outside was was gazing in wonder at the stars.

It was the ideal accommodation for the showman. The fresh air blew away the alcohol and the nicotine, and it was extremely handy for the toilet. I woke refreshed the next morning with a raging appetite fuelled by the exquisite smell of sausages and bacon being cooked on a stove outside the Austin Hotel.

In spite of that fond memory, this year I'll be in a hotel without wheels. It will have sheets on the bed and hot water in the bath. It won't be the same... but honestly, I believe it will be better.

£16,000 was the big snag

AS YOU read this I will be starting to bale my silage. That is, if the monsoon has abated. Isn't it quite extraordinary how our weather fools us? A month ago it felt like it would never rain again. Then we got the rain just in time to save this year's crops. And a fortnight ago we had had enough and were looking for the sun to fill the pods.

But it doesn't work that way. My neighbours have been making silage soup for a fortnight and I'm hoping hard that the sun shines this week. Our beleaguered cattle need a bit of luck and some good silage for the winter would be a start.

Mind you I was proud of my fellow beef producers last week when they met on Bogieside for the Royal Northern Agricultural Societies annual Beef Event. An estimated three thousand of us met at Cairnborrow farm near Huntly, to view 600 hectare beef-arable family farm. There were a hundred trade stands, some very good cattle of ten breeds and permutations of crosses, demonstrations by the machinery and beef trades and by the colleges, speeches and rain.

And what was it all for?

It was partly educational of course and I did learn a bit. About a thing called a "Bacfact", for example. That's an aid to marketing cattle, sheep or pigs at the right time. You just massage the beast's back with a "sound sensor" and a computer does the rest. The visual display unit shows you a picture like a gaudy lino tile from a cheap showhouse. If you are as expert as the salesman you will be able to interpret the colours and know exactly how deep the fat is – and how big is the eye muscle. End of those arguments with the graders.

There only seemed to be one snag with the Bacfact (apart from its awful name) – it costs

£16,000. The salesmen were not so daft as fail to realise that price was not their strongest selling point however, and suggested that it is really a tool for the contractor. They reckon that such a service should soon be available at 65 pence a scan.

Then there were two Piedmontese-cross-Friesian calves and their foster mother. It was a most impressive pen that. They were five months old, four and a half hundredweights and tall growthy beasts. They looked a bit like a cross between those other Italians – the Romagnola and Chianina. If they can deliver what they promise – easy calving off the dairies – there may well be a place for them.

There was a muckle Aberdeen-Angus bull there to show how the scope of that breed has been increased recently. We were asked to guess his weight and I said at once, "1350 kilos." Of course it wouldn't be a round number like that so I wrote down 1349, thus doing myself out of a valuable prize.

The only other prize I noticed was awarded to Gilbert Scott for his magnificent effort in bringing no fewer than 39 of Sir Dennis Mountain's cattle to form the Simmental breed's exhibit.

There were a hundred other things of interest at the beef event, but nothing much that we couldn't get at the other summer shows.

Except this; The cattleman's day out was wonderful for morale. The cheery way the three thousand were accepting all that was happening to them, and their determination to put anything right that needed it were a tonic. They renewed all our faiths in the essential goodness of our product as a food and its unbeatability as a feast.

And by the way, you will remember my kind neighbour Mossie taking the wind out of my sails when I was blowing about my six foot high crop of rape? He said it would all go down during the week of the Highland Show. Well, for once, Mossie was wrong. It has gone down already. I could have wished for him to be wrong in a more convenient way but one has to be thankful for small mercies.

July 2, 1990

Mad cow disease keeps livestock values down

MY INVESTMENT in livestock is creeping slowly up in numbers though, thanks to BSE, it is static at best in value. We have 131 cattle to enter in the June census. And I am very glad to say we have a whole new livestock venture, for I have fallen heir not just to one but to two donkeys.

Gina and her yearling son Dominic have come from a distant cousin who has given up his croft and didn't want his cuddies to go out of the family. That suits me fine for, being in fierce competition with the other side for the affection of our grandchildren, there is no doubt having two cuddies

Turnbull.

GINA, MAY I INTRODUCE YOU TO 'GURGEDYKE JOCKIE THE FOURTH'!

DOWN BOY!

gives us a distinct edge.

Now Dominic, being of an age when boy donkeys will start to be boy donkeys, and Gina not being with foal, the first job was to get her to an unrelated stallion. It so happens that our butcher has such a stallion and he proved easy to deal with at a forty ouncer of malt whisky.

So on Sunday I was on the road waving goodbye to Dominic (who seemed to sense that he was being done out of something) and setting off to walk Gina the two miles to her holiday field where Gurgedyke Jockie the Fourth had some free time on his hooves... and was waiting.

It may not have been the most important job I did last week but it was certainly among the pleasantest and, as we clipped and clopped along the little road among the glorious broom, I was able to reflect on the irony of my mission. Our cattle are currently in the midst of a state-of-the-art breeding programme in which we are taking ova from heifers at the slaughterhouse, fertilising them in glass with Simmental sperm and implanting the resulting embryos into our Jersey cows. Yet here I was taking animal breeding back to the days when there was always a horse on the road to a coupling, though with the horse it was usually the stallion who did the visiting.

And I remembered the day ten years ago when I took a bull over part of the same route to a neighbour's cow.

Daisy was a Shorthorn-cross-Ayrshire which provided milk for the house as well as for her own calf and three others. She was six months clear of her calf and still not pregnant despite regular visits from the bull with the bowler hat. As Sandy said "The A.I. is a' right when it works but it is a damned expense when it disna."

Sandy had asked me to bring one of my "funcy bulls" so I chose Glen Prosen who had been Champion at the great Turriff Show. Surely that would be funcy enough.

We were pleased to be striking a blow for traditional breeding methods and I felt it right that Glen Prosen should do his courting in his best clothes. I shampooed him, gave him a blow dry and combed his hair up with a little three-in-one oil so that he gleamed in the sun. We were a magnificent sight as we swung along the road... me and my 14cwt doggie on the halter.

As we passed the crofts on the way anxious neighbours peeped out, for news of our trip had gone before and children had been warned to stay in lest they be gored by the wild bull.

Round the last corner we went and into the neat little close where Sandy and his sister Polly were waiting. And there was Daisy rinking enthusiastically with a little Friesian heifer she had for company. We put Daisy and Glen Prosen in a loose-box and retired to the house for a business dram.

Soon we were sneaking back to see how the contract was progressing... but I'm afraid it wasn't. Glen Prosen had, of course, no idea what he was there for except that he could see that it was an occasion of some importance. And even though she had had ten calves Daisy had never been through that door either, as all had been by artificial insemination. There they stood, back to back, and looking distinctly bemused.

Polly was sure that nature would find a way so we retired to try another dram and discuss the decline in the moral standards of the youth of the day.

Still there was no success and while nature might indeed have found a way given time, we were impatient and decided to let them outside to rejoin Patricia in the field. Perhaps a menage a trois would be better.

Indeed it was. Being back with her playmate seemed to settle Daisy and the extra dimension fairly tickled the bull.

So we had another business dram to celebrate and then we had another because we had acquired the taste for it.

When the bottle dried up I caught my bull, waved goodbye and set off for home in the glorious sunshine. The young bull gave never a backward glance but his step seemed to have a firmer assurance as he strode rhythmically along. As the sun beat down on us I put my arm across the great wide back and resting my head on his soft warm flank I shut my eyes and floated along. I could have slept on my feet right there.

In her own time, Daisy had a fine heifer calf which topped her section at the store sale at Maud. Glen Prosen went to Perth where he made me nineteen hundred guineas to add to the drams I earned when I introduced him to Daisy.

I hope the mating of Gina will be as successful. Certainly the welcome she received at her holiday home promised a successful outcome.

One day in the life of a rich and famous farmer

DO YOU read those articles in the glossy Sundays in which the rich and the famous let you into the secret of what they do in an average day? If you do you are probably as amazed as I am. No wonder they are rich and famous.

The R&F are either liars or they get up at five-thirty, do half an hour's yoga, read at least four daily newspapers and write at least a thousand words of their autobiography and do the housework in time for a working breakfast with their agents at half past seven.

Well, I had a day like that last Saturday. I bounced out of bed, in response to my alarm which was set as usual for 3.30 am. As I waited for the kettle to boil for my early morning tea I wondered if there could be this day a repeat of those fabulous events in February when farmer Jeffrey and half the Edinburgh grain trade took revenge for Flodden at the battle of Murrayfield.

On that day the Scots had won the "walk on" ten-six, they had then pulverised the English in the national anthems fiftyfour-nothing, and then (holy of holies) they won they game as well. So could the lads do it again far away from their own wee bits of hills and glens?

Of course there were none of the glories of the battle of Murrayfield but they were up against a team that was so much better than the Auld Enemy that I was overflowing with pride at their three tries when I went out at five to "observe oestrous" in my Jersey cows.

You see we are about to transplant beef embryos into them and, so that the transplanter only has to come the once, we had given them an injection to make them all run on the same day. For reasons that I don't understand the success of the job depends on seeing exactly when they are in standing heat so the earlier I got a start to it the better.

There was no doubt that the injection had worked for when I got down to the field it was like (I imagine) a blue movie. The girls were all milling about jumping on one another while others queued up or tried to mount the jumper.

Our little donkey foal, who has been with cattle long enough to think himself a bovine, tried hard to join in. He hadn't really the height for it and the cows were quite clear that it was none of his business and gave him a very hard time.

A yearling steer had a better reception. In fact when the sexiest of the cows called time-out to suckle her two calves he was able to join in that too.

I then went round the stock to find that no disasters had befallen my other six fieldsful of cattle and checked the barley, wheat and rape for all the insects and moulds I am beginning to know by name but have never seen, and then set out with my wife for our daughter's birthday party in Dundee.

I always feel sorry for travellers who are not farmers. When they go on a long drive all they see is the road. But farmers have constant fascination in what all the opposition are doing in their fields, mile after mile.

On that count I must say the trip was something of a disappointment; everything was looking so well.

Or nearly everything. I could hardly believe it when, in the Howe of the Mearns, I came across some setaside. That was an unsightly shambles which I wouldn't have enjoyed anywhere. But in the Howe of the Mearns? That is some of the finest land in the world. A rich finger of prosperity, it points up from the plump hand of Angus, as though to mock the poor stony ground we have to farm in Aberdeenshire.

When we were growing thirty cwts of barley they were complaining if they didn't get fifty. So now that even we are growing three and a half tonnes, what could the Howe of the Mearns produce? I know all the good reasons for setaside but surely, not in the Howe. If there are farmers there who cannot make more than £80 an acre from their land, would they not step aside themselves and let someone who can have a chance?

The party started with a football match which revealed the full extent of my arthritis and reminded me of what an athletic as well as determined creature my wife had been when I met her thirty years ago.

And it was a proper match with goalposts, two teams (Dundee and The Rest of the World) and a ref. who I think should have been at the world cup. What was so wonderful about this lady was the way she handled one of the galaxy representing Dundee.

This young man had turned out wearing a pair of those long baggy shorts which seem to be in vogue with our colour blind younger generation. They had, I think, been made from an old pair of his grannies curtains and patched with an old frock from my grannies generation.

Anyway, when this young man got the ball and, showing some talent for the game, came rushing down the park the gallant referee immediately blew for a foul and penalised him for what I believe to be the new offence of "unnecessary posing". Two minutes later he was yellow carded for "persistent unnecessary posing". Yes they could thole a bit of that in Italy.

It was then time for the barbecue at which I'm glad to say the BSE burgers we had brought vanished like snow off a dyke, proving either that the young have a healthy scepticism or that they can't read.

And so to the second emotional pounding of the day; the match between Scotland and Sweden. Even after that I didn't seem to be tired and my typical "day in the life" didn't finish until everyone had sung a bit of every folk song a bit of which they knew.

Change out of £1,000 at the Highland

I HADN'T been down at the Show long when I bumped into Mossie. He has all sorts of good social reasons for going there as well as casting his eye over all the expensive hardware on show. I like to cast my eye on it too but that's all I can do... though when I see something I fancy (like almost any of the new tractors) I like to daydream that in ten years time the model may have drifted down into my price range.

Big Hamish wasn't at the show this year. He says he's feart in case he buys something he cannot afford. It's a pity for we saw just the machine for the farmer who likes to have everything. It was on the Ford stand among the tractors though it looked more like train with a lum like an old-fashioned steam engine.

An enormous hunk of hardware, it has three hundred and twenty-five horse power and it must take at least a hundred of the horses just to move the machine itself. I don't really know what a "maximum operating weight" of fourteen and a half tonnes is but I could see that it was a lot.

They sell "seven or eight" of these monsters a year but I'm afraid I won't even get one after it has suffered ten years of depreciation. It's called a "Versatile 946" but it is so unversatile that it couldn't even get into our fields with their twelve foot gates. And with a height (to the top of "the exhaust stack") of eleven and a half feet it couldn't get into any of our sheds and would have to be outwintered.

The price? Well, Fords aren't boasting about that. The Versatile is what they call P.O.A. which stands for "price on application" and means they aren't telling Tom, Dick and Harry who appear at their stand

and obviously couldn't afford a lawn-mower.

However reading between the lines it appears that Big Hamish saved £80,000, or thereby by staying at home. And he must have made the right decision. The Versatile is no good unless it's pulling a ten furrow plough or an equivalent and has a turning radius of 170 feet. On the poor bumpy land here in the North East you would need half of most parks for endrigs and with a pass as big as that there would always be at least one plough clear of the ground.

Nevertheless there were those who were contemplating the investment. One told me he counted it like this; "I would like a tractor like that. But I would need to sell the farm to buy it. And if I sold the farm I wouldn't need the tractor."

Anyway the Versatile was never in any danger of landing at Little Ardo. But I did buy one piece of new machinery... my first Highland Show purchase on capital account since the year I forgot to pack my toothbrush. If one or two small financial details can be ironed out there will be a brand new auger for boring strainer holes on it's way north.

It will give me change out of £1000 so it's hardly a major investment but even at that my fear of overdraft at 17.5 % is so strong that I counted it all very carefully... and then bought it anyway.

I have eight strainers to take

anyway.

I have eight strainers to take out in the next few days to fence my silage bales, and apart from that I might put in another four in an average year. Now James Low, the great grieve who terrorised this farm for over forty years, used to say that, if the job were to be done right, it would take a man a full yoking to dig and fill a strainer hole. But then he worked in the days when everything had to be done in the most difficult manner possible and had to last for ever. His strainers were quite suitable for tethering the Queen Mary, though they were never near enough sea.

"Auld Low" as he was known (not always with affection) wanted the spade to be totally out of sight but I always reckon that if you get it in to the handle you're not bad and if there is no one looking you can take off a bit more. Better still, now that we have a power saw, I can dig my hole until I hit a stone or get fed up, plant my post and then sned it to whatever length seems suitable.

On that basis I reckon that a man like me, especially if there is no danger of having to prove it, could take out all twelve holes in two days. At that rate my purchase is worth two days work a year. But the auger will cost me £175 for the borrowed money and be knackered in six years, so I need to get £300 pounds a year off it. Now even in the pub I can't claim to be worth £150 a day.

So how do I justify my purchase?

I am going to make my machine available to the Buchan Machinery Ring. Fellow members will queue up to pay me thirty pounds a day for a hire. Soon my auger will be taking out the holes for half the fences in Aberdeenshire.

And if that won't work I'll just have to be honest and say that the reason for this purchase is the commonest one for all machinery... I want it.

Salmon poacher of note

"WATER, WATER everywhere and not a drop to drink" is my text for today. For while what I have been describing (with perhaps a hint of exaggeration) as "the monsoon" continues, the North East in general and Little Ardo in particular is still very short of ground water.

We have for many years had three sources of supply and of those only one is running. Were it not for the new well we dug last year we would have to let some cattle go, or let some of the four houses stand empty, for even my great grandfather's well, which he said would last forever, is down to a trickle.

And yet the heavens have opened daily and the crops which last year were crying for a drink are verdant, heavy and sinking fast. Just when the sun should be filling the raw green berries the rain is pushing them down towards the swamp.

The situation is by no means desperate yet, indeed if the sun shines well in the next two months we could still have a record harvest, but it is beginning to get worrying. As Mossie predicted, the best field of rape is now all knocked over although it still isn't quite "as flat as a bannock" and the heads are still above the mud. And, while all the winter barley is showing some lodging, only one field is over fifty per-cent flat.

The annoying thing is that for all we are getting the rain we still have so little in the tap. The old men are right again, to fill the well you need the snow. Rain just fills the burn.

Not that that's a bad thing for the poor old Ythan's in a terrible state. The nitrogen we have been laying onto the fields ends up growing weeds in it, the silage effluent makes further calls on its oxygen, and with the three years since we had anything like a winter the water's so low there's hardly a clean fish in the burn. Not a single salmon has been taken.

It was not always so and it is said that there used to be so many you could ford the stream on their backs.

I don't know about that but I do know that my great grandfather had a well merited reputation for poaching them. At that time the sporting rights all belonged to the laird so that, though the river ran through his farm, John Yull had no right to a fish. And he had no need to poach for, though a middling farmer, he was a successful auctioneer and could buy a fish any time he wanted it. But my great grand-

father was full of devilment and would have a fish... and often.

On a celebrated occasion in the early nineteen nineties John Yull was fishing with the "Ythan Fly". That's an ordinary wire snare more often used for catching rabbits. You make a slit in a freshly cut stick about six feet long and wedge the snare in the slit. The snare has a string on it long enough to run down the stick and wrap securely round your wrist.

John Yull had spied this fine eight pounder (for he didn't like them too big and course) underneath the rock that overhangs the edge of the water at the bend near the start of what is my

stretch of the river today. He eased the snare over the fishes tail very carefully lest at a touch it shoot off upstream. Then, with the snare in place, he let go the stick and hauled as hard as he could.

Out onto the bank flashed the gleaming silver captive, sea lice still on her as she thrashed her last on the bank.

John Yull had not been alone on that day for he had with him his daughter Mary, who almost fifty years later became my grandmother. There is a picture of her as she was that day. Sitting on top of her Highland pony, pretty in her long black dress, brown hair in ringlets and about to enter her teens.

She was supposed to be looking out but was far more interested in the fish and so had failed to warn of the approach of the water baillie.

John Yull looked up too late to do anything but curse his luck. There was nowhere to hide the fish and it was now dead and would surely float belly up if it were thrown back in the river.

It was then that my grand-mother showed for the first recorded time, that poise and assurance which was to make her a legend in the North East over the next seventy-odd years. "Gie's it here, Dad," she said, and, concealing the fish under her flouncing dress, she turned her pony for home.

"Good-afternoon, baillie," she said with just a hint of haughtiness, "isn't it fine to see the sun."

Of course the baillie knew well where the fish was, but those were gentler days, and there was no way he was going to challenge the integrity of the skirts of Miss Yull of Little Ardo.

When I look at that old photo of the lassie and her pony, and remember the serene old lady who could hold a first rate Hogmanay party in the 1960s without offering her guests strong drink, I am filled with wonder. And when I think that she is now dead and gone, not just from the farm, but from everything with which I can identify, I am filled with a sense frailty. It makes it hard for me to believe that anything endures except our land.

The day I put the beautiful people to work

I HAVE made remarkable progress in the fight against wild oats. I refer not, you understand, to that metaphorical crop which holds such a fascination for so many in the sowing but which is so unpopular in the reaping, but to the cereal weed about which no one has a good word to say at any time.

The wild oat is a relative of the poor thin oats with which our forefathers used to eke out their existence in the eighteenth century and before, and, when we look at those weeds towering above our rich barley and wheat crops, we should surely pity those brave men and women. For it is a miserable plant ideally suited to its life as a weed. Its seeds are so small that the plant can hold as many as a hundred of them up above the competition, and yet you would need hundreds of seeds to feed a kirk mouse.

They are becoming quite a problem in the North East where the local College advisers are warning farmers to be increasingly vigilant against wild oats. They've been called out to fields with as many as 150 plants per square metre. That means a considerable yield loss as well as the possibility of making harvesting more difficult.

It's easy to believe the wild oat is thriving. As I drive through Aberdeenshire and Banffshire I see more and more crops with a patch of hairy green standing proud of the ripening crops. That's sad enough in itself but some of the reasons for the growth of the weed are sadder still, for they are symptoms of decline.

Unless you have a really bad infestation the trouble isn't going to be in the current year but in the future so that if you are faced with spending £17 an acre on spraying for wild oats the temptation, if you are hard up, is to cut down on the spray. And that seems to be what has been happening. Most of the bad cases are where someone is in difficulties and has had to call for professional advice or where someone new has moved into a farm when the for the oats with the added advantage that the farmer can't see them.

Well now, about this time last year I had been pontificating to my wife about how the right way was to farm as though you were going live for ever. We'd also been discussing the progress of the wild oat so,

previous tenant has finally lost the struggle.

The swing to winter cereals hasn't helped as the seeds are ploughed under in the back-end instead of lying out all winter a prey to birds, mice and frosts. Then again, for the last few years, there haven't been many frosts to help with the weed control. And the spread of oil seed rape won't be helping. It provides an ideal environment

knowing I was doing nothing about it, she became distinctly worried. "It's like you think there's no risk of you lasting more than a year or two. Certainly the way you're carrying on with that digger the steading won't."

With those cruel words, "Action Woman" set off for the fields and wouldn't let any daylight pass until she had rogued all one hundred and forty acres of cereals. I even joined her some evenings when she came home from her job in Aberdeen and I must say there are a lot worse ways to spend the sort of bonnie summer evenings we had last year.

Unfortunately, Fiona is too busy for the roguing this year, or the weather is too vile, so it seemed the good work was not to be kept up... until last week. Then we had an invasion from a young couple with champagne habits and skimmed milk incomes whose financial planning was based on the premise that tomorrow could only come by accident and that the day after had no chance.

They were in desperate need of funds for more champagne and ignorant enough to think I would give them. Then I had the sort of stroke of genius that is not given to many. I would fee them to rogue the cereals. Not only that, I would get them to count the stems they picked though I knew I would have to do the division to find out how many weeds we had to the acre.

Remembering how long it took Fiona last time, and full of the advice "you don't make much difference in one year because the seeds can come up in any of the next seven", I offered a pound an acre for the 120 acres we have this year.

I suppose I should be glad to say that I seriously overpriced the job which was very far from being my intention. I was flabbergasted when, towards the end of the second day, the bright young things came and claimed their money. Surely they had missed out a field or two... or maybe they hadn't rogued them properly. But no, all was done.

And the reason was simple. There weren't nearly as many weeds as last year. In the field that had been best last year there had been not one wild oat. In another big park there was only one to the acre. In another there had been five to the acre and another there had been about twenty. The worst field did still have too many wild oats to count but you couldn't have made one stook out of the ten acres.

So Fiona had done well last year and, at a pound an acre, I think we'll manage to keep the ground clear in future. The sad thing is the young couple won't get more than ten bottles of champagne for their work. If only I could persuade them to be more realistic and drink beer... but that is dreaming.

Local bus is hero of the day

OF ALL the institutions and individuals who have been pressed into service on this farm over the years we surely had the most spectacular this week. It was the Fyvie to Methlick bus... and a double-decker at that.

Being a one-man band I am always storing up jobs for the moment when somebody appears... the travelling salesmen are so used to getting a bull's head to hold while I do it's feet or having to give me a bump start with the old tractor that they have stopped calling. It's not every farmer who would say this but I do miss them. And of course I always have to get a squad together for any of the routine cattle jobs.

You'll maybe remember the squad I had for my herd test for tuberculosis and brucellosis. Then I had arranged for a retired mechanic, an oil-man on his fortnight off, and the chemist from the next village (we call him Potions). That

worked not too badly. Potions, who is young for a chemist, ran about with great enthusiasm and did what he thought he had been told. Willie the mechanic knew what he had been told but was slow. And, despite the fact that the oilman didn't turn up we got the job done. We always do.

Well, this week it was the first of the cattle going fat off the grass. That is, of course, my favourite part of the grazing season, putting my product off to market is the culmination of such husbandry as I have exercised. But I always dread the business of taking them in to draw them. That just can't be done alone so there must be a squad.

Absolutely our worst situated field is called "The Admiral" after the retired admiral who built a bungalow in it. Out of the ten heifers there there were three fat and, as it involved a mile's droving, half of it through the village with all

131

it's tempting gardens, I decided to try to draw the cattle in the field to avoid the return journey.

I took down a trough and half a dozen gates to the Admiral and was fixing those into a sorting pen when Potions the chemist appeared. To cut a long story short he had been waiting for me in the close and was not amused. He didn't seem to be aware that it was in the evening that the squad were supposed to muster and he insisted that it would have to be now or never. "I'll go for Gowkie", he shouted and disappeared in his Mini.

He was soon back, not with Gowkie but with Willie the Hunter, the man who shoots at our pigeons. By that time and by great good fortune I had managed to select the three we wanted. Against my better judgment, against all the advice of history and chronically understrength we set off.

Just how badly equipped we were was plain even for the enthusiastic Potions to see when we came to the cross roads by the river. Worse than that, one of the corners is the entrance to the Admiral's house so the absolute minimum squad there is five.

Luck was with us however for the Admiral was taking a delivery and the delivery man kindly manned the gateway. Then we had to run the gauntlet of Blackcraig...a street of twenty houses more than half of which have gates and several of which have walls that are better for looking at than keeping cattle out of the shallots.

The plan, if what went on can be dignified by such a word, was that Potions and Willie would go in front to take turns of filling the gateless openings. I took up the rear with the car.

But there were just too many gateless openings and I found myself having to jump out and fish the brutes out of garden after garden. And when I did, of course there was only my car to stop them making back to the field. Again the delivery man came to the rescue. He came along behind me and right up beside my car. I was about to abuse him as one of those wreckers who cause stampedes among driven cattle by insisting on getting by, when I saw his plan. The two vehicles quite filled the road so that from then on when I got them out of the next garden they couldn't turn back.

We may not have been quite "Highway Code" but we made brave sight two-a-breast, the

estate car and the delivery van, on the road to Fyvie.

Many gardens and some picturesque language later we made it to the farm road after which all would be plain sailing. And then we had some more luck. When we passed the field where the fat stots were they all came running to see the girls. Now I had tried three times earlier to get those stots out of that field for worming and failed and was dreading the attempt this time. But when they were gazing lovingly up the road after the heifers I was able to nip the gate open and they all followed us up the brae. Job done.

Or so I thought. For when we were putting the stots that weren't fat back to the field the one that had been causing the trouble earlier jumped in amongst a field of younger steers. We decided he was as well left there and dispersed to lunch with that satisfied feeling that the job wasn't only done but well done at that.

As it happened, it was far from done. I had just finished the soup when a red faced man appeared at the door. "If you've eight Charolais stots they've broken oot and they're awa' ben the road to Fyvie". The jumper had shown his new pals how to do it and they had all jumped out and off.

One man has no hope with eight stots so it was with that sinking feeling I set off in pursuit. Down the farm brae and onto the Fyvie road. And it was about half a mile along that that the double-decker Fyvie to

Methlick bus had come to the rescue.

There he was droving them back to me, lights flashing, horn tooting and weaving from side to side as the principles of good droving dictated. I was able to reverse to the farm road and await the return of my prodigals.

July 30, 1990

The day I put my foot in it

I AM filled with optimism this evening as I sit at the window of the converted corridor I call my office and look out across the Ythan valley to Formartine and the blue outline of Bennachie. The first grazers off the grass sold to 121.6 pence a kilo liveweight, the crops have been getting the sun they were needing, the vat man found that I had only claimed £322 too much tax back since 1986, and the visit of two of my granddaughters is almost over.

And I have found that one of our best institutions here in the North East, one which for many years seemed to be under threat, is in very good heart. I refer to the New Deer Agricultural Association's Summer Show.

I was at the Show forty-four years ago at what must have been its centenary event. At that time it seemed a worthy stolid affair; apart from the din of the carnival it all seemed very quiet and dour. There were cattle there to be judged and, as you would expect in the heart of this cattle country, lots of them. But there was no pretence at entertainment. There was no commentary to explain things to the people. The public address was only used to announce the winners, and that long after the competitors had left the arena.

There were a few heavy horse at that time but few sheep for this was the heart of an area that prided itself in its fat cattle and was just along the road form the birthplace of the Aberdeen Angus and the farms of Uppermill, Collynie and the Pittodrie which had made fortunes from the Shorthorns.

That may have been some sort of heyday. Certainly I was very pessimistic about the Show fifteen years ago when I wrote that it had degenerated into a sort of glorified pony club. I was exaggerating, of course, for the hardy folks with their feeding cattle were there still. But there was only one representative of the leading breed in the country then, the Herefords and a handful of Blacks and no Shorthorns. The biggest class of pedigree cattle was called "Any Other Breed". (I beat off the challenge of a Charolais and a Dexter to win that with a Simmental) The ring was quite taken over by pigtails and overstretched jodhpurs.

What a wonderful change on Saturday. There is still an Any Other Breeds section but there are now classes for Charolais, Simmentals, Limousins and Belgian Blues and the Aberdeen Angus are still holding on. And sheep? There were three hundred and twenty entries including classes for Charollais, Rouge de L'Ouest and Texels. Those of us who feared that the show would one day be devoted to the horse as a toy were delighted to find that it is now so busy that the pony club activities have been banished from the ring to a neighbouring field.

The New Deer show has a down-to-earth character. And that's best illustrated by the fat cattle section. Those are judged as carcasses but also on the hoof, though unled. That means the farmer doesn't have to go to all the commercially irrelevant bother of washing, blow-drying, hair-conditioning, clipping and halter-training. The beasts are simply taken out of the field on show day and penned to ensure captivity.

That means that what is on show isn't something bred and produced to win honours in the show ring but a selection from the best cattle that would be going to Maud or Thainstone markets that week or direct to the local abbatoirs. And the existence of such a class brings forth a large number of entries from men who wouldn't dream of buying a hair-dryer... except perhaps for the wife.

Anyway it was a great day and it was made better for some by my putting my foot firmly in it. I had been surprised by the heifer which won the Simmental cattle championship. She was a good beast but she had five tits which traditionalists like me consider to be one too many. Now also in the ring and standing third in line was that excellent stockman Gilbert Scott with a bull that I judged he would have expected to win with. As he was leaving the ring I tried to tease him with. "Now now, Gibby, imagine being beat by a five titter".

"She's mine too" he said, somewhat tetchily, "and what's more I've got one at home with six and she's had six calves in three years".

My gas wasn't at a peep for long... how could it be at the show at which I spent most of the 1980 event chasing two of my Simmental bulls round a field of barley in full view of everyone, including the owner of the field?

It was great to see the show that I had won my first serious money as an athlete in such good heart. That was in 1953 when I used to get half a crown a week pocket-money. I came home from New Deer Show with four pounds (enough in those days to fee a middling farmhand for a short week) and thought myself a man.

And I met one at Saturday's show with an even fonder memory of cleaning up at New Deer. Bill Rennie has a daughter who in 1946 needed £11 to go to London to further her career as a dancer. The family had newly moved into and stocked one of those Buchan farms which is too small for anything except ambition, and the family didn't have a bean.

They couldn't pay their gate money to the field but they couldn't back-up either because of the traffic behind them and were eventually let in. The lassie did well in the Highland dancing, her brothers won everything with their Highland ponies and some more in the foot-races. And on Monday morning, when they took her to the station to wave her off to London, the dancer had £14 in her pocket and some change.

137

Drier trouble at harvest

THE FIRST day of harvest has (as increasing numbers do say, I'm afraid) came and went. And eagerly as it was awaited so were we glad to see it go. There was good news and bad and I'll start with the bad...

Of course the stuff wasn't really ready but when all your neighbours are panicking it's hard not to join in. At any rate, we thought it would be a good idea to try the field that was nearer to being ready than the rest... it would give us a chance to see that everything was working perfectly and give everything that was going to break down the chance to do so before the big rush.

To that end the big day worked a treat.

It had been a week's work getting everything ship-shape; the silage pit for the wet grain, the silage pit for the very wet grain and the barn for the dry stuff all swept up. The holes in the barn floor, which had provided a dripping roast for the rodent population last year, were all cemented in and the drier all greased and bursting for action.

Of course our drier is the main source of worry. She's a mobile model of which you may well not have heard. She is to grain driers what the ark is to navigation; historically interesting as the last throw of a desperate people, but somewhat obsolete. Those facts being well known there was little competition when I bought the old Morridge at a roup. I thought she looked cheap, and as long as you feed her a generous diet of shear bolts, I think maybe she was.

Potions, the local chemist who has his business so well organised that he can come and play at farmies with me, was beside himself with pride that he was to get the tricky and responsible job of driving the grain home. That would mean driving the cart alongside the moving combine at just the

right speed and at just the right distance to catch all the grain… no mean feat in a wind. I assured him he would manage.

He did too and, as he brought home load after load, his demeanour became more relaxed and you could see that he was really enjoying himself. On the sixth run he casually mentioned that he hadn't lost a seed.

But the next run home was without the cart I'm afraid. He'd cowped the four ton load on the face of the brae… in full view of the village and to the barely controllable delight of the good people of Methlick. Only if you have tried to pick it up from among stubble and straw will you have any idea of just how much barley four tonnes is.

Luckily the combine, with fully five acres cut, retired with a badly damaged reel so we didn't hold him up any. And it is just as well we did have those hiccups for I was not doing well with the drier.

The old girl was devouring shear bolts at an alarming rate and eventually stripped all the pinions off the new clutch I had had fitted to the loading auger at a the end of last year. That job had cost me £320 and, determined to save myself most of that this year, I dashed the 16 miles to Kintore, got a replacement and fitted it myself in a couple of hours.

I was well pleased with myself and the money I had saved when Mossie, the great cereal grower arrived. He had with him another of the grain Barons. Since the days a dozen years ago when farmers here about used to say "one nine for a copy" instead of "how's it going" he's retained his handle "Red Rooster".

I am always in some awe of crackshots like Mossie and the Rooster and I'm sure you can see why. I was just about to allude to my engineering success when Mossie stopped in his tracks, pointed and exclaimed, "T'hell's happened to that clutch".

"It's nae on straight" said Red Rooster.

And with that the two of them were under the drier, backsides in the air, shaking their heads puzzling earnestly as to how the situation might be retrieved. They soon had my work undone.

"Gie's a shot o' yer emery paper, Charlie."

"Oh, but I have none."

"Well pass me a file."

"I think we did have one of those but..."

"Oh well at least gie's a shot o' yer cloth."

Before I could say I'd run and see if there was one in the house Mossie's daughter piped up,"I think they just use their trousers here Dad".

It was all a bit irksome and that was made no better by the "peep-peep-peep" from the Rooster's pocket which announced that he was required on the telephone. Some say he gets the exchange to call him every half an hour just to impress lesser persons like me but there was no doubting the seriousness of this call.

The swather he hires out had broken down, or so he thought, though he could hardly hear. At six foot four he wasn't quite high enough for good reception. So he started to climb. Soon, face as red as his hair, he was standing on top of the cab of the power unit (ex-corporation lorry) and bawling words I haven't heard since I was at school. I am sure British Telecom would have refused to handle them had they been given the option.

Anyway having reduced me to a quivering jelly the two great men moved-off. The Rooster had managed to clean the drive shaft with the sandpaper on his match box. That had been a great success and

140

the clutch now fitted perfectly. I was of course very grateful but mostly because they had gone. Only because they had gone in fact for the old girl somehow managed another shear bolt as soon as they were out of the close. Two days and three expensive call-outs later the drier is still in bits.

And the good news I promised you? We have only done our worst field and, though we won't have a final figure until we can dry it, we have definitely got above three tonnes to the acre.

August 13, 1990

Can't beat Mossie for blawin'

WHAT A JOY the harvest is being. I don't want to tempt fate but really we could hardly have been luckier up till now. The stoor has been flying out the back of the combine and the black reek pouring out of the tractor as the heavy loads are hurried home.

Mind you the yields haven't been quite as good as last year so far. Our first field of Pastorale winter barley ran 3.17 tonnes to the acre and, though the Pleasante which we cut second was a little better I don't think it was as good as last year's 3.3. My hopes though lie with some Ermo, still to cut as I write. It's a six rowed barley which, though late, looks very promising.

I expect you're pretty impressed at the way I am reeling off the names of those barleys. Well, to tell the truth, I have been boning up on those details since a particularly painful humiliation I suffered last week at the hands of my two barley-baron friends. When Mossie

and he were sorting out my drier, the Red Rooster asked me what variety the barley in the drier was. My answer was the best I could do. "Eh... this is winter barley" I said, to peels of happy laughter which I thought a little unkind.

Why the yields aren't away up I cannot imagine for the weather has been as near to perfection as I can imagine. Each season brought it's bounty of rain or sun in turn and just when we started to look for a change we got it.

But, if the yields are down a little, there are two useful compensations this year. First the price is better. The one load of feeding barley I have sold made £105 ex the farm, as opposed to as little as £99 last year. And secondly, drying charges are minimal. The wettest we combined at was nineteen and a half per cent and I don't think we got down to that last year. And three quarters of it is below 16 per cent. We aren't drying that at all. Unless the wheat comes in wet the fuel companies are going to have another poor year.

The next test is the rape. Despite all the desperate prophesies it looks perfect. Even the stuff that was down was still up enough to let the swather in and, as that was done in damp mornings when the plants were rubbery, we didn't lose a pea. I

He is thinking of removing every second wire from the concave in an effort to let the seeds through or, failing that, he's going to get hold of a pea viner for his best 200 acres.

Of course it's not everyone who has got off as lightly as me in the drying of the grain so the usual resentments are building up against the grain merchants.

am now openly hoping for a tonne and a half this year for the first time... and secretly hoping for more.

I have even tried to impress Mossie with the success of my rape-growing but he is a hard man to beat when it comes to blawin'. His crops are apparently so heavy and the peas so big that he doesn't know if the combine will be able to cope.

Like, "why is it that, if they quote you a price of ten pounds a tonne for drying, when you get your final returns back it always turns out to be eleven pounds or more?" Everybody knows the answer, (they quote a charge on the tonnage arriving at the drier not the weight after they have shrunk it down to the tonnage they pay you on) but we don't have to like it.

to the tonnage they pay you on) but we don't have to like it.

And the shrinkage that takes place in the drier. Why is that always so great? If I put grain in at 25% and they dry it down to 15% surely they have just thrown away the 10% that is water they don't want and I should be paid for the 90% that is left? The ten tonnes I put in should now be nine, should it not?

Well, bitter experience has taught us all that shrinkage is much greater than that. In fact in that case of a ten per cent reduction in moisture content our ten tonnes will have shrunk to eight point two tonnes and no power on earth will persuade us that the grain merchant hasn't stolen the missing sixteen hundredweights. After all, there is plenty of precedent for that.

Although there are some pretty sharp characters among them, I don't really think the grain merchants are as bad as that. Indeed now that I dry my own barley I can see that the shrinkage is genuinely a bigger-than-expected phenomenon.

When I first started to take an academic interest in shrinkage I came up with the theory that the percentage that we are talking about in our grains is by volume not weight. So, to throw away ten per cent of the volume of the crop by drying involved throwing away more than ten per cent of the weight. That would of course depend on the water being heavier than the solid matter in the grains.

I was in some excitement about this discovery and would explain the point to James Fowlie of Auchrynie, a wise man who is about as hard to beat in a discussion as Mossie is to beat at blawin'. James almost floored me for a start by pointing out that, in his opinion, the solids were heavier as, if you put some grains in a pail of water, they sink.

With the sort of originality I would like to become my hallmark, I resurrected my argument by countering that if, on the other hand, we poured the bucket of water on a heap of barley, the water would sink to the bottom proving that the water was the heavier.

He wasn't convinced... and neither was I.

144

Painful memory o' hairst

IT WAS 1947 on a farm within a hard bike run of Huntly and the harvest was being won with great difficulty. The second tractorman was a strong man and willing but even he had to give in to the most appalling toothach. Willie Thomson (for that is a name that would have suited him quite as well as his own) had been suffering on and off for a month or more but, with the onset of harvest, there had never been time for the dentist.

The day came however, when, right in the time of the leading home of the sheaves, when the matter could be postponned no longer. Thomson's face was badly swollen and after a night of stouning agony he decided he must go to Huntly, harvest or no. And leaving the field in the leading was a matter that he would not undertake lightly. After all there were just the five in the squad; one forking the sheaves onto the carts, one to build the carts, two to drive the loads home and fork to the grieve who built the stacks. Four just wasn't a squad at all.

Thomson started with the others at seven and did an hour setting up the wet stooks that had fallen down in the night and then biked the twelve miles to Huntly. When the dentist opened at nine he found a man in terrible need. He could neither stand nor sit for the pain. There was no time for an aneasthetic but after pulling two healthy teeth the dentist got the one that was abessed. Bleeding profusely and with the towel round his head the greatly relieved tractorman set off to bike the twelve miles back to the farm.

It was a slow business as it was mostly uphill and he had to stop to be sick from the nausea and the blood he had swallowed. Nevertheless the second tractorman was home in time for a cup of tea before joining the rest of the men in the harvest field at one o'clock.

Nothing was said.

Not, that is, until nineteen years later. The same two tractormen were still at the Mains and so was the grieve. The farmer was still there too. But times had changed. The squad at harvest time was no longer five. All that was needed was a combine driver, somebody to drive home the grain and somebody to be toon-keeper and mind the grain-drier.

All the other work was being mechanised and the Mains was clearly overstaffed. One of the excellent trac-tormen would have to go. It gave Mains no pleasure in the asking, for he knew they were both good men, but one day at their daily meeting after lowsin' time he asked the grieve which of the men they should put away. Without a moment's hesitation the grieve said that Thomson should go. "What can you do wi' a man that goes awa' in the middle o' hairst?" Elephants and grieves never forget and certainly do not forgive.

I tell you that story, not just because it illustrates how hard the hard men were, but as a sort

146

of chest-bearing excercise. You see, right in the middle of my harvest, I have been away, overseas at that, and not for a morning but for three days.

I had been invited to say a few well chosen words at the dinner that rounds off the Orkney County Show.

What a pleasure it was to be back in the Orkneys and how I admire the farmers there. When I arrived at the ferry that was to take me from Scrabster to Stromness I got my first reminder of just how difficult their row is. I approached the ticket counter with my loose change at the ready to discover that they would need almost twenty pounds a passenger. I explained that I didn't want to take my car but that was indeed the fare for going on foot.

I met a farmer there who told me of the expense of getting his cattle to market. He has to pay for a float to take the beasts to the ferry that takes them to the Mainland (of Orkney). He has to pay the ferry and he then has to pay another ferry to get them to Aberdeen from which they need another float to Inverurie.

And it's the same story for their supplies coming in. The show park was ringed with rather natty galvanised steel gates of the type the Cheap-Johns have been hawking round the farms of Aberdeenshire at about forty-five pounds a piece if you stick in. But those gates cost sixty five pounds on the Mainland and goodness knows how much on the outer islands.

How lucky we are in Aberdeenshire that we avoid those expenses but how much luckier that we don't have the wind and the sea spray and that we can grow a variety of things. While our beef production is in the doldrums we are getting some joy from the winter barley and great joy from the rape. But beef is practically the Orkadians' only crop (though the sheep are increasing).

And yet they are both smiling and doing a wonderful job. The cattle at the show were looking very well and the star classes were the black cows. Where else could you see sixty black cattle on show and only three Simmentals?

The stars were a huge Canadian-bred black heifer and a wonderfully fleshed but active Shorthorn bull. To the great consternation of some of the traditionalists the cow got the supreme award. The judges, all from Scotland, thought her size and mothering potential made up for her being narrow in every respect except the amount of the park she took up while moving her back legs. Late into the night one of my hosts was still shaking his head and saying he never thought such a bad cow would ever win Orkney Show.

And my words of wisdom? Well I told my hosts that not many could survive as they had, and I told them they had my great admiration. And I illustrated the point with the following practical suggestion.

After the current difficulty in the Gulf, Saddam Hussein should be banished to the most remote of the Orkneys. He should be given a croft with an overdraft of five hundred pounds an acre, be entirely dependent on P.& O. for his supplies, have to buy his bulls from Ronnie Sabiston and sell all his stock through Aberdeen and Northern Marts. That would be a considerable deterent to future dictators.

I don't think my hosts were impressed.

Snippets from a Prophet called Mossie

KINGSCLIFF SPORTING Lodge is a remarkable phenomenon. In quieter times it was the small and undistinguished farm of North Ardo, where, for many many years, a gentle man called Geordie Mackie looked after a byreful of stots and his few hens.

When, as happens to even the oldest men, Old Mackie was finally called home the farm was bought by one of the oilmen who flooded into the North East to earn the King's ransom the oil companies called wages. Some of the land was sold off and that might have been the end of such glory as North Ardo had enjoyed.

But in the mid-eighties hard times came to the North Sea and the oilman found that he was faced with the choice of unemployment or leaving the area. His next move was a masterstroke. He bought himself some clay doos, some traps and a pool table, applied for a licence for the barn, and North Ardo became the Kingscliff Sporting Lodge.

Now the air is filled with the sounds of clay doos being shot, or shot at, all the daylight hours. And when darkness falls, in the barn where Old Mackie fed his stots, the modern farmer of North Ardo harvests a crop which would surely have made the old man's eyes to shine. It is a most exemplary diversification.

To some, the old barn is a place to refresh and postmortem the clay pigeons which have been shot and those which have got away. To many it is just another boozer. But to we of the Methlick and New Deer Agricultural Discussion Group it is the venue of the Sunday evening meeting. And to me it is even more than that. It is my Mount Sinai where the Prophet Mossie lets slip snippets of the Truth about how to grow the five tonne crop of wheat, the four tonne crop of barley and the two tonne crop of oil seed rape.

There I sit like a child of Israel waiting for the light to shine on me.

I tell you all that because, this week, I found myself in a rather embarrassing position in respect of my third and last field of rape. My first two fields, one of Cobra which grew to be sixfoot six high and seemed to be far the best crop, and one of Tapidor which had looked far the best all winter, both yielded thirty-three cwts.

Both were after winter barley which seems to be the orthodox rotation. But, encouraged by last year's success and egged on by the Prophet Mossie who has some eighth year rape doing well, I decided to put in an extra field of Tapidor as a second rape.

Heads were shaken. I would get all kinds of diseases, every-body else had tried it once and it had been a disaster, and I would have a disaster too... I would see. And you got the idea that this was a disaster that everybody else was going to enjoy.

There were times during the growing season when a disaster looked the most likely outcome. I even had a soil sample analysed to see if there was any reason apart from being three weeks later in the planting why the second Tapidor should be so patchy and so far behind. The college had no chemical explanation to offer.

At any rate, by harvest time, it was clear that my second rape was not going to be a disaster as long as the weather didn't get it.

We got it sixteen days and about three inches of rain after

150

swathing and by that time the tramped endrigs were into muck and some of the stems that were sticking up had turned white but it was clear that there was going to be a crop.

It isn't really a good thing to count the cart loads to try to estimate how much you have. It is a funny thing, but it doesn't matter how honest he is before his peers and before his Maker, when counting cart loads at harvest time, with no-one to deceive but himself, the farmer will always exaggerate his crop. We should just have patience till we get the returns from the mill.

But there is nothing much else to do as you wait for each load. With rape the loads are fewer and the waits longer... so we count.

We have a five tonne Weeks cart and I know what 2.45 tonnes at 16.7% moisture looks like because that was the dribble that was left last time and I took it over to the mill myself.

I reckoned seven loads would give me 30 cwts and that would certainly be a great happiness and show them that it wasn't just the Prophet who could grow second rapes.

It soon became obvious that something had gone far wrong

with the counting. I had four loads with only half the field cut. I started to sweat with embarrassment as the count rose and rose. Greg Henderson from Nethermill has already posted a 37 cwt crop this year but it was clear that, by my count, that would be left far behind. I decided not to count one load to make the yield look more realistic.

And yet, when the field was finished and the rain lashing delightfully down on my neighbours crops, I had 36 tonnes off 17 and a half acres... fully 41 cwts to the acre. At twelve per cent that would dry to 39 cwts... after a pint or two the two tonne crop could be on.

How embarrassing that that should happen to be Sunday. But I am too old and wise to boast to the discussion group on the basis of my cart loads. I even went home early when I felt a blaw coming on. After all I didn't believe my own calculations.

Thank goodness I held my uneasy peace. My 36 tonnes turned out to be 33 and the moisture metre we had kindly been lent should have shown 19 % not 12. My record 39 cwts turned out to be just over 33.

Still, not bad, eh?

September 3, 1990

A delightful legacy

IF ANYTHING marks the farmers of Scotland in general, and of the North East in particular, out from normal people it may well be our infatuation with anecdotes. Remarks and pieces of repartee which others can find trivial or incomprehensible are treasured, retold again and again and inflicted on every succeeding generation.

One such has been much on my mind this week and it is because I have made a delightful discovery. It hints at immortality.

But let me remind you of the anecdote.

It concerns a well-known family who farmed near Ellon. They had the reputation, well earned over many years, of growing the best neeps and the finest corn for many miles around. And their's was a very public success for every farmer who passed that way to the Ellon Market on a Monday or to catch the train to Aberdeen on a Friday must pass the three good fields that lay down to the main road.

And old Hilly, who gloried in that reputation, cheated a bit. All the muck that was ever made at Hillhead went on those three fields so that, with the seven year rotation, there would often be one field of rich dark green grass, neeps that were coming over the dyke and the heaviest corn for miles.

As happens with the cycle of death and renewal that is the peasant's lot, the day approached when Hilly would retire and young Hilly would take over. That was a day for which young Hilly yearned, for he was fed up of hearing what a great job his father made of the place. He was fed up too of being the lad who did the work and when he went into the market bar was told by all and sundry that he would never be the man his father was.

Conversely old Hilly had no great wish for retirement. With the passing years he had accumulated enough excuses in the way of lumbago and his sore knee to take the toil out of farm work… what was there to retire from? And he liked his reputation for being the best farmer in the district.

Nevertheless Hilly did retire eventually and with a very poor grace. The young man took up the reins with enthusiasm, though without parental encouragement.

That was at the November term and by the next September there was a fine field of dark green grass, a fine crop of neeps and a heavy and clean crop of oats for the farmers to marvel at on market days.

Young Hilly started to take on a swagger and tell folk at the mart that they should now see that he was every bit as good a farmer as his father had been. But generosity of spirit has never been a common characteristic of the Aberdeenshire farmer and there was none of that about when old Hilly caught his son in the act of blawin'.

"Are ye sae blin' that ye canna see what aa' body kens. I'm standing in these parks yet."

He was right of course. Ten years of young Hilly's stewardship proved it. For by that time those three fine parks were no better than good average.

But the concept of standing on your farm after you have left it… of your good work surviving you… is close to the essence of the peasant's relationship with his land. I don't know what it is. Less dour folk would call it love, but whatever it is I feel it. It was my father that first told me that anecdote and I know he felt it. So, if what the ministers have told us is true, he will be sharing my delight at what I discovered at Little Ardo this week.

My father was a good husbandman. He was generous with the muck and never banged on the nitrogen when an excuse for a compound could be found. In his time the dykes were kept up, the weeds were kept down, the drains were kept open, the roans were kept up and the overdraft was kept down. John R. Allan didn't do what all his five brothers and sisters-in-law did and sell the farm on a leaseback to finance high farming.

To that extent he is still standing in the parks at Little Ardo.

But he made a far more enduring contribution. When he came here in 1945 he found one of the barest farms in the Thanage of Buchan, which is famous for bare places. The

153

dozen scraggy trees round the steading were scant protection from the wind that howled down from the North Pole without obstruction.

John Allan, with what he was kind enough to call "help" from his small son, set about creating the place as it is now, a somewhat ramshackle steading with a beautiful house set among a delightful variety of trees. When he planted those trees there were many old heads which were shaken "funcy stuff like that'll never grow at Ardo" they said. They were right sometimes, but not always. The poplars were an instant success, though they are dying young, and the willows which protect the footpath down to the village are the most effective shade as well as giving us catkins for the house when we are beginning to tire of the daffodils.

Between those willows and the rowans which are such a show just now, there are a dozen trees which till this year I thought were pretty boring though, being bushie, were good against the west wind that howls down the Ythan Valley.

But I know what they are now. For they have produced the most delightful and abundant crop of plums. They're sweet too with perfect skins, and there are at least two trees bearing greengages, though there are those who say they are just yellow plums.

When my father came here the best you could hope for was an occasional raspberry in a sheltered spot on a south-eastern side of a dyke. But he left us a legacy of fruit trees on what had been one of its barest faces.

He may no longer be standing very tall in the fields at Little Ardo but John R. Allan stands yet in its hedgerows.

The Golf crisis

EVERY morning, these days, I thank my God and my bank manager for the fact that I do not have my own combine.

What brought me to this particular act of faith was a run up country. My contractor had brought his £90,000 monster which had gobbled up my twelve acre field of Ermo winter barley in under three hours when I set off to see how everyone else was getting on. It was a beautiful day and every combine was in the field.

But what struck me was how few of them were moving.

Indeed by far the most of them were broken down, their proud owners in the guts of them, or bawling down their CBs for engineers or spare parts. You could almost say that, if a combine was moving, it would belong, not to the farmer, but to the contractor.

That's as it should be for a new combine can only be justified by the grain Barons or by contractors who have many acres in their books. But the seductive thing about the combine is that the £90,000 monster will look a snip at £25,000 after three harvests and after ten it will probably be available at £5,000.

There's a good reason for the depreciation and I don't want to know about it. Breakdowns always happen of course but it makes the best of sense for a smallholder like me to let the contractor worry about them. And because he does worry about little else at harvest time the contractor makes sure he has a machine that won't break down often and that he has the spare part when it is needed.

I have a neighbour who was held up for and extra day when he got so annoyed at the breaking down of his bargain banger that he threw a vital washer and split pin (which would have fitted eventually) away into a grass park from which it was never recovered. He shouldn't have listened to the salesman... they always tell you about the "one careful lady driver" but they forget to tell you about the "kamikaze pilot, the matador, the three soccer casuals and the prop forward".

At any rate the harvest has gone pretty well so far. With only the wheat to go, we are ahead of budget. Mind you, not everyone is having a great harvest. Mossie isn't saying how

good his yields are, so we fear the worst... below four tonnes of barley and two tonnes of rape even. And of course Big Hamish has had a middling harvest as far as the rape is concerned.

You will remember how grateful we were that he kept so many thousands of pigeons well fed through the winter. At the mart unkind people with loud voices have been asking him if that was a field of setaside. But he bore that cheerfully and when his crop did come away late it was with pride that he was able to get an out-of-season discount from the swather.

You will recall that Big Hamish has a £27,000 digger and a £30,000 tractor so when the day came for the combine we really shouldn't have been surprised that he had an artic standing by to take away the seeds.

Well, I'm sorry to report that the artic represented something of an overkill. There were seeds all right and not just "black gold" as they are calling rape. Hamish had a good mixture of daisies, fat hen, docks and poppy in his cart... eight tonnes of them off his twelve acres. It has to be said that that is more than expected and the big man intends to catch up further by selling them as "organic". He should have no difficulty in persuading intending buyers of their authenticity.

There is a good deal of quiet spite being directed from this part of the world towards the whisky companies who have been buying so much of their malting barley from out of the places like England, Denmark and the Lothians. We've great crops of malting barley this year but the distillers are showing hardly any interest.

However, I'm glad to say that Big Hamish has managed to corner a buyer and get a load away at £122 a tonne. He has found it very hard to keep that one a secret I can tell you.

It's nice he has something to blaw about for he got a terrible shock this week. Not being a reader and preferring music cassettes to the radio in his cabs he is not an expert on current affairs. It was at the discussion group on Sunday night that Big Hamish overheard sombody referring to the "Gulf Crisis". Now Hamish who grows fifty acres of Golf naturally thought there was a critical shortage of Golf barley seed and that his fortune was to be made again.

As we explained what we knew about Saddam Hussein the face fell as realisation dawned. And then he brightened up again and a determined smile emerged as Hamish contemplated getting the digger ready for war.

In the meantime it is make-your-mind-up-time on what to sow for next year. We've put in fifty two acres of oil seeds and they are through the ground and looking well. But I am swithering about another field. There is no doubt it is by far our best paying crop again this year but the trouble is that we are not the only people to have noticed. In fact everybody from Rothicmurchas to Eastern Siberia seems to be ploughing up another parkie this back end and putting it into rape. It is worrying. Perhaps it is time to get back to the rotation that is best for the farm and stop trying to be too clever.

We shouldn't forget the well worn advice that we should spend on the land as though we were going to die tomorrow but farm as though we were going to live forever. I'd much rather spend it on the drains, on the steadings or on the weeds and let the contractors spend the megabucks on the machinery. And God preserve me from owning my own combine.

Limousin was our star turn

I WANT to give you an update today on how my hundred and thirty cattle are getting on.

Let's start with the stots that my livestock consultant Sandy Fowlie bought for me on the spring day. I got ten away this week and they really did very well. They had put on 134 kilos a piece averaging, with the beef special premium and after mart expenses £623 against a buying bill of £505. In a year like this that is surely a good outcome.

It's not all good of course, for I have yet to deduct Sandy's commission on the purchase and it was left that we would "see about that once we see how they get on". That's confidence for you.

The star turn was a 625 kilo Limousin steer which sold for 114.6 pence a kilo. That was surely a "good beast" on Sandy's scale of three, rather than a "decent stirk" (as he was supposed to be) and none of them turned out to be "plain brutes". And that's just as well for there is a far bigger difference in price between what is good and what is plain than there used to be. Ten pence would one day have covered the best and all but the very worst.

I proved the change myself on Wednesday at Maud for I was also selling a steer called "Friendly". He was a Shorthorn-cross Ayrshire which was sold at a neighbour's roup. There is a tradition hereabouts that you always try to buy something at your neighbour's roup and I would buy this petted beastie. But Friendly turned out to be much more Ayrshire than Shorthorn and he brought up the rear at the fat ring at 81.6 pence a kilo against 104.1 for the rest. It does rather look as though Mr. Fowlie has earned his commission.

It was also an extra-ordinary thing, I thought, that the biggest steer also made the highest price per kilo. What-

He SHOULD ENTER HIM FUR THE GRAND NATIONAL!

Turnbull.

ever happened to those "handy weights?" It used to be that the small cattle topped the sale, the mediums came next and the monsters had to make up in kilos for a distinct lack of pence. I expect it is because so much of the good stuff is going into intervention and size, there is no barrier. It must be a sad blow for the British native breeds which have been used to claiming higher prices per kilo.

Anyway, if the star was a Limousin, so was whatever you call the opposite. As soon as we appeared to take those cattle in for the market he came scampering up to see us. But when we opened the gate to let them out it was he who led the charge to the other end of the field. Three times we got them up to the gate and each time our Limousin friend, lugs pricked, head and tail up made for the far end of the field at a rate which would have done fine in the Derby. Perhaps I should have said "Grand National" for at the end of the third charge he cleared the fence and landed among the silage bales.

That proved a great help, for the other stots came in no bother. The Limousin had no problem jumping out from among the bales and landed three fields away among my younger stock. He's a good beast and will make a fine carcass... and the sooner the better as far as I'm concerned.

Incidentally, one or two of the discussion group have expressed surprise that I put those stots to our local market instead of the new mart at Thainstone which seems to be sucking cattle in from everywhere. Well, this centripetal force seems to me a pity. We even sing about our own mart here.

"Oh the streets are paved with gold they say in London

But that's a place I wadna' want to stay.

Tak me back tae Maud a place where I'd' be happy,

And the streets are paved wi' sharn on Wednesday."

The Charolais and Simmental steers I bought last spring to multiple suckle the Jersey cows are looking well but slow. It looks like they will finish at two years rather than the eighteen months I had been kidding myself on about.

And the Jersey cows themselves? Well they are very sweet and I am very fond of them but I am beginning to fear that the milkier types are not going to be tough enough for my job. For the second year running they have had a mysterious eye-lid problem; the lids turn raw and need daily attention, they've taken turns of the respiratory disease IBR, and mastitis has been a bad problem. That has hit even suckling cows and one late calver got mastitis which didn't seem to bother her much until it killed the calf and septicaemia from the calf killed her.

On the other hand the transplanted Charolais which had the Jerseys as surrogate mothers are doing well enough to give hope for the ultimate success of the system.

And Lottie, the twisted faced heifer I brought over from Jersey is thriving. She is maybe not putting on weight but at least she is holding her own despite the constant attention of the two Limousin who just about match her five hundredweight already. Unfortunately she was thought too thin by the bull with the bowler hat and has shown absolutely no inclination to reproduce again. Having had a night out with the' bull in Jersey and landed in calf as a youngster seems to have put her right off it.

Lottie seems to be like an old friend of mine who had just the one child in the days when that was unusual. He said, "I tried it once and just thought nothing of it."

The grieve who done well after a shaky start

I WAS was talking the other day to a former minister of the crown. Now you may think me a bit of a name-dropper but this chap was my grandfather's grieve here at Little Ardo sixty-six years ago. He's now the Labour party's spokesman on agriculture in the Lords but at that time he was just John Mackie, aged fifteen whose main ambition in life had been to make the first fifteen at the Grammer School but who had had to leave to be grieve at his father's new outfarm.

When I think how young I was at fifteen, and how young my sons were at twenty and how young so many are at twenty-five, I marvel at the pressure it must have put on young John suddenly to find himself in charge of five men in a man's world. Indeed legend has it that I am right to marvel and that the pressures were well illustrated by what happened on his first day.

On such a day it was imperative that the young grieve get off to a good start... that he stamp his authority on proceedings from the very first.

In those days of stable etiquette the men would line up to get their orders at two minutes to six. The foreman stood first, then the second horseman, the baillie, the orraman and the loon. The grieve hardly slept a wink in the short night as he rehearsed how he would give the orders. The foreman and the second would yoke their ploughs in the byre park, the orraman would yoke the orra-beast and go to Kelly Sawmill for a load of backs. The baillie would take his tapner to the swedes after he'd seen to the cattle, and after he'd done the hens the loon would sweep the close.

Well might the young man worry. At half a minute to six he entered the stable, his stomach making a middling job of coping with the heavy knot of brose that had been his nervous breakfast. "Aye," he said and set off at speed down the line giving out his endlessly rehearsed orders.

It was a fluent performance, by all accounts, and accomplished in record time. But when the grieve had finished the horsemen had been told to yoke their tapners among the neeps, the baillie had been sent to Kelly for sticks, and the or-raman and the loon had been sent to the sacred plough. It was an inauspicious start but it is said that the men knew fine what the laddie meant and, in a

show of humanity unusual among the farming folk of the North-East, they did as they should have been bidden.

And happily John Mackie's progress in farming was unimpaired. In a few short years he was farming at Bent, the best farm in the Howe of the Mearns, and he is now laird of the historic Harold's Park which, when he bought it, and with the traffic conditions prevailing then, was said to be but twenty minutes from Covent Garden.

It's a handy address for John's public speaking improved so much that as well as

162

farming he was able to pursue a political career which saw him an Agriculture Minister, Chairman of the Forestry Commission and now Lord John-Mackie who opposes the government in the Upper House.

He doesn't just worry about the great affairs of state all the same. When I spoke to our old grieve the other day he was trying to be brave about a grievance we all share against the grain trade.

His wheat was coming off the combine at 13% against the trade's requirement of 15% moisture. John-Mackie had tried his merchant for a higher price for this grain pointing out that if he had been 2% over the limit they would have penalised him so, as he was 2% under, they would be being no more than fair if they were to compensate him in like measure. There is little doubt the millers would be mixing the dry with the wet saving the drying charges and the shrinkage they'd already recouped from the person whose grain was too wet.

At two per cent over you suffer more than three pounds a tonne shrinkage and as much as another four for drying charges so you would think those who dry too far would get a little

something. But no. "That's not how it works", said the merchant.

Of course we all know that, but is it fair?

John-Mackie also told me that his old friend Richard Rodenight had a machine for putting back the water if his grain was overdried. What a splendid idea. I'm sorry he didn't patent it. For I put away 26 tonnes of barley at 12% earlier in the year and at that I would have been quite entitled to pour getting on for two hundred gallons of water in over the cart.

That was something like eighty pounds right down the throat of the merchant and it does emphasise how important it is to get everything just right in this difficult farming business of ours. And selling as much water as you can at £105 a tonne is definitely part of that.

It can lead to trouble though, if you try to fly too close to the wind. A friend of mine (who must be nameless for reasons which, I hope, are not too apparent) got a very red face this week when he tried a little bit too hard.

Disgusted that the previous two loads had been given a reading of under 14% moisture my friend determined to sell a scoopsful of undried wheat. It had come in at 18% and averaged over the whole load would still leave a margin on the buyer's side. However by Sod's law, and for reasons which no one could understand, the sample wasn't taken, as is usual, by the automatic dipper which takes a couple of pecks out of the middle of the cart. The driver was told to start tipping and the sample was taken from the first lot to come out...the undried stuff at the back.

"18% . Get that stuff out of here."

What a waste of time. The load simply went back to the farm, spent half an hour being thoroughly mixed in the unheated drier and reappeared at the mill where it read 14.6%.

Tank at Gight smiddy

FOR their own reasons the army have chosen our little neck of the Buchan woods to practice defending the realm against the Queen's enemies.

They have charged around in vehicles of great size and speed and adopted dispositions aggressive and defensive, and been a source of endless "speak" in the community.

Gowkie, had just finished looking round the ten hill cows that are his farming enterprise when he was astonished to see a tank at the Gight Smiddy. It was taking up an unfair share of the close and had its gun pointing "fair at the hoose door". Or so he said at the shop when he went in for his paper. "Aye the smith'll fairly hae till pay his poll tax noo," he told them.

Big Hamish also had a visit

from a tank. He found them in his tattie-shed. Now you will recall that he is the man who thought the Gulf crisis was something to do with the shortage of Golf barley. But the discussion group had told him all about Saddam,

"Fit are ye deein' like?" Hamish asked the tank crew, conversationally.

"Hiding from the enemy."

Now despite our tuition Hamish still had little idea of where Iraq was, though he knew it was well south of Stonehaven. "Still," he thought, "if these boys are hiding from the enemy and them got a tank I'd better get my plant under cover". So he rushed out and got the £27,000 digger and Jumbo (his enormous Ford 7710 tractor) into the safety of the tattie shed.

Hamish was impressed with the tank. I don't think he'll rest happy until he has one of his own. His cattleman is leaving and I wouldn't be surprised if cows and quota appear on the market and a Chieftain comes home to Weetingshill.

And the big man wasn't the only one who spotted the agricultural potential of the tank. Mossie was making one his prairies for winter barley when this tank rolled up and asked permission to romp about over his ploughing. "Well I couldn't have stopped him". It was before we had all that rain and the tank commander was able to get something of the feel of the desert as he stormed about the powdery earth. But Mossie was thinking creatively. Would he not just couple the tank up to the power harrow and give the boys an honest day's work?

Not everyone enjoyed the soldier's visit though. The Red Rooster, our other grain baron, is a man who sees no point in driving at eighty miles an hour if you can see your way to doing the ton (or the tonne now that he has gone metric). But you can't get much above forty when your stuck behind a tank on our narrow Buchan roads.

That can be infuriating if you are a busy man like the Rooster so, when he did eventually get past, he stopped and gave the commander as good instructions as he could as to how to get to Baghdad.

Not since the days when we were deaved by the low fliers has the military made such a mark on the district but it has to be said they they did a superb job of their public relations. All the farmers upon whose land they wanted to play were invited to a reception at which vited to a reception at which they were shown round a military establishment and fed all the food and drink they could take. It was such a success that Big Hamish swore that if this was the army life he would enlist.

The fliers, though, just didn't seem to know how to do it. No doubt there were those among them who cared but I have twice heard young men describe the routine of holding the phone out so that all can giggle at the outraged complaints of those who have been shocked by illegal low flights. I myself found my mother cowering down in her garden after some young man had shaved our treetops. She thought herself back in the blitz.

The other military matter which set the village ablaze concerns one of my most interesting neighbours. As well as sharing my abhorrence of pouring good money after bad on expensive agricultural machinery, "The Colonel" as he is known, keeps the village amused by his court appearances.

And the Colonel's latest court case has surpassed all that has gone before as far as we gossips are concerned. For he has pled guilty at Banff Sheriff Court to several firearms offences including assaulting five people by "presenting an imitation firearm at them".

As usual in such matters there are two versions of the truth.

The procurator said that when a man to whom the Colonel owed wages had appeared at the door the Colonel had produced a facsimile gun. The man left and phoned the police.

The Colonel, who had recently retired with that rank from the Terriers, told it rather differently. When at half past nine at night a car load arrived at the farm he thought he might be under terrorist attack and he scared them off with his imitation firearm.

The court preferred the fiscal's version and fined the Colonel £300.

But the discussion group aren't finished with the case.

You see the Colonel also admitted having a five-shot pump-action shotgun which wasn't included on his firearms certificate. Now the worrying thought is that a man with thirty years training in defence matters, who thinks himself threatened by the IRA, should chose to defend himself, not with the pump-action shotgun, but with a replica.

Why I need another pair of hands

BECAUSE I have no staff here I like to call myself a one man band. I see myself like the street entertainer who plays the mouth organ, accompanies himself on the guitar, has cymbals between his knees, a drum he can kick and castanets under his oxters. Certainly that's what always comes to mind when I am drying wheat, a lorry comes with feed and I can hear the phone ringing. I don't answer for I know it will be a neighbour to say I have cattle on the road. I wish I had another pair of hands... like the one man bandsman who would like to play the clarinet as well as everything else.

Although I still have no staff, I have to tell you today that the Little Ardo One Man Marching Band now has the means to play another instrument.

It's all due to the Buchan Machinery Ring from which I have been able to hire, at a very reasonable rate, a brand new Armstrong.

The Buchan Machinery Ring has just completed its first year and there's never been anything like it in the North East. It's not a new concept, that's as old as the hills. We used to call it "neeporin'". It worked best among small farmers where two would put their horse together to make a pair and plough each farm by turns. The grandest expression of neeporin' was the thrashing mill which went from farm to farm and required a dozen neepors to get together at each farm. And of course there are those modern silage groups where one will own a fine modern cart and another a four drum mower and a third the laser precision chopper.

But the machinery ring is

the neeporin' principle taken to a high degree. The aim is no less than making every machine in Buchan available to every farmer in the Thanage.

They're well on the way too. There are already 150 members among the canny and independent-minded farmers of the North East Corner. You can hire a combined harvester, with or without chopper, dutzi, tube-liner, bike for spreading slug pellets or a sheep dipper... all with or without driver. You could also hire a grass topper from the ring or a post-hole borer but there is no demand for those. I know for I offered mine to the ring and there hasn't been a bite yet.

That's a pity for the ring is not just a way of reducing the capital cost of farming. It is also a way of justifying that which is so many farmers' hobby and pitfall. How many have indulged their desire to possess huge machines which are shiny and new and have found that the bank wanted their money back when there was none left to give?

The Machinery Ring lets each farmer concentrate his cash on a few shiny machines the cost of which can be lubricated by hiring them out to others in the ring. It works well

for most people. What a pity everybody else in the ring understood that the only post-hole borer that is much use among Buchan's stones is the spade.

No such problems with the Armstrong. It is a machine in the greatest possible demand and it is easy to see why.

The Armstrong can act as a gate or a dog. It can activate the bruiser, drive a tractor, discourage salesmen and feed barley to the cattle or shear bolts to the grain drier. All this it does without the usual great expense in diesel, gas or electricity... all the Armstrong needs is a plateful of soup at dinner-time and a few words of praise now and again.

You see, the Buchan Machinery Ring also provides labour. Farmers who have too little to do can offer themselves for hire by the hour through the ring. My new Armstrong is called Jim.

He is a considerable citizen. He's got a big whisker which he grew during his 27 years in the Royal Navy and has the sort of confidence that command can give. He was, in his time at sea, quarter-master on the Royal Yacht and Chief Gunnery Instructor on the HMS Blake. He must have instructed

them well for his lads claim seven Argentinean planes shot down in the Falklands war.

All that was of course done by computer which was ideal training for tying up gates with bale twine, hand mucking, and chasing Limousin stots about the countryside.

The Armstrong has another virtue above my other machines. He is a considerable storyteller and, for all I know, a considerable maker-up of stories for the telling of.

My current favourite of those concerns the time in Singapore when leading-seaman Armstrong was on funeral duty and had (what was to have been) the honour of laying a wreath on behalf of the ship's company. There were ten or so other tributes to be laid and, as Sod's law would have it, our man was to be last.

It was monsoon time in Singapore and had been so for some weeks. That having been so, the Colony having a reputation for landslip, and the quality of gravedigger being not of the best, a dozen matelots marching up slamming their great boots to attention was too much for the soil structure. When Jim crashed to attention the side of the grave gave way and he landed in it.

The officer who had charge of the choreography of the event was distinctly unamused and Jim is unlikely to forget his face bearing down on the over-filled grave. "I told you where to put the wreath Armstrong and it wasn't in the grave". Jim tried to tell me that there were some stronger words used as well but, of course, I didn't believe him.

I did however believe that Jim's accident gave the widow one of her few happy moments in that unhappy day and that she had the grace to laugh out loud. I believe that because I do believe it. And anyway only a fool spoils a good story by "wonderin' gin t'were true".

Trying to limit the damage

A fortnight's rain has left us with much to do. And the object isn't to catch up. That is impossible. All we are trying to do is to limit the damage.

The rape is more or less all right though a small part of one field did blow away in those awful September gales. But the winter barley is a month behind and still in the bag. It would be nice to be finished the wheat and yet as I write we haven't started. My crops consultant, who isn't paid to be cheerful, says we are losing yield with every day that passes.

Apart from worrying harder there isn't a lot you can do, and yet I have caught one field up by what I consider to be a brilliant ruse. It may yet turn out to be a bit of agricultural pioneering. I have decided to grow a field of perennial rape.

The Byre Park was due to go into winter barley. But things being so far behind and the volunteer rape seeds growing in such profusion and so evenly, I decided just to leave the park as it was. We have now sprayed it for weeds and various fungi and, instead of another park a month or more late, we have the furthest-on field of rape in Aberdeenshire.

Of course I am only saving, say, forty pounds in rape seed and contractor's charges for sowing them so it mightn't be a good plan in a good year. But the point is that we failed to get the stuff in by conventional means so the perennial rape seems worth a try.

If I am proved to have been wrong (as with so much of my pioneering) at least we still have the alternative, on the spring day, of malting barley.

As the Monsoon continued and as an alternative to looking dismally from the tractorshed or hiding in the house we have been getting on with one of my projects. It is one about which I feel rather sad and also very guilty.

We have been dismantling

my barley-beef factory.

A mere fifteen years ago that had been my pride and joy. It was a super concept. I would feed twenty cheap calves in at one end of the factory every month and put twenty fine fat cattle away every month. It was to be the equivalent of the milk cheque. I would buy calves at £100, feed two tonnes of barley and put £2000 into my pocket every month.

It was a slatted shed for 150 cattle with a 200 tonne silo next door with a bruiser house complete with mixer. An automatic feed line would mean I could meat all those bulls from the comfort of my bed if necessary.

It was a proud day when, in 1975, we filled the shed. It was the first new structure on the place for thirty years and had cost eight times as much as my father had paid for the title deeds.

With the benefit of hindsight I don't think we should have been celebrating. Far from being the end of our trouble the barley beef shed was just a new beginning.

We spent the first week retrieving them from all over the country. If you cram bulls into a pen with nothing to graze they work away with their tongues until they undo the most complicated of catches.

Eventually we did fool them with spring clips and chains.

But there were plenty of other troubles. The feeding system was just too complicated and never worked. The continuous flow principle which the economist in me thought would please the banker was all right on paper but as the bulls flowed clockwise through the shed so every germ that ever entered flowed anti-clockwise back to the young stock.

We lost ever so many to pneumonias of various kinds and of course those were the early days of IBR. Then there was the business of tramped tails. It was an evil thing that and for some reason it was only a problem among bulls. Having nowhere to lie down but the concrete slats there was always some tail being stood on. That usually went septic and death was common. Often we were treating several in a pen at once.

Then there was the trouble we got into with the grain tower. We became more and more gallous about how wet we would cut the barley and were soon chancing it at thirty percent. That worked fine and was really popular with the bulls until the loon forgot to close the hatches and 150 tonnes of grain went into a lump. It bridged about ten feet up and we were then faced with the highly dangerous job of trying to get it to fall down without burying us. One method which didn't work was discharging the twelve bore up into it.

Anyway I've decided that the slats are wrong and that my brave new factory is a white elephant and useless.

So with all this time on our hands as rain stopped our other play we've been doing away with the slats. I've found a buyer at five pounds seventy pence a slat and I'm converting one side of the shed to a bedded court. We'll give then a ramp to the other side where we'll retain the slats. That will give accommodation for say fifty beasts eating and drinking at one side and resting on straw on the other.

I do feel guilty about it. The £38,000 that went into the elephant was about 40% government money.

Perhaps I could present this move as my extensification programme. I could also say that it is a matter of animal welfare. The truth is I am making the best of a bad job.

YOU LOSETH YIELD WITH EVERY DAY THAT PASSETH!

CROP CONSULTANT REPORT: GLOOM DOOM

AH KEN HE'S NO PAID TO BE CHEERFUL, BUT THAT'S PATHETIC!

Traveller's tales from the East

THERE IS a farm in this part of Aberdeenshire which is famous for the size of its fields. It's called Cairnadailly and, as suited the six year rotation which survived till the 1960s, the 320 acres are divided into just six fields. The biggest is getting on for 60 acres. I am often thankful that I was never sent to that park to "pu' neeps" on a frosty morning.

It is said that a ploughman, new to the place, got lost in one of those great prairies. It was foggy when he set off to set up a feerin'. The first job was to set up his props, so he left the horse and set off with his spade to make the marks which he would follow and so keep the first furrow straight. On and on he walked but never reached the top of the huge park. Dumfounded, he thought he must have gone through a gate at the top and be in the wrong field. In panic he dropped the spade and tried to find a dyke and get some bearings. They

say that, as the fog lifted, the rest of the men were entertained to the sight of Willie casting around, trying to win back to his pair.

There could just be a hint of exaggeration in that story, and I only tell you it because I have seen this week where losing a pair of Clydesdales would be easy.

Behind with the work or not the farmer would have a holiday. Or to be more precise, the farmer's wife would have a holiday and the farmer would have to go too. Not that he minded that, but it did look bad going off with so much barley and the wheat still to sow.

The trouble with holidays is that they have to be booked up in advance. You choose a time which you think will be a quiet one on the farm and then get reminded about the best laid schemes of mice and farmers.

Anyway, we landed in Budapest, capital of Hungary, the country which is leading the charge of "Former Socialist Countries" as they like to be called, into the Common Market. There was ever so much culture about in Budapest but the farmer wasn't happy until he had hired a car and was out in the country looking at the kind of culture with which he is most familiar... agriculture.

As I have said before and as I fear I will have to admit again, farmers from my part of the world know of no greater joy than seeing the opposition making a poor job. In that respect there was plenty to warm the heart in the part of Hungary that lies on the Rothiemurchas side of Budapest.

Of course being October there wasn't a full grown crop to criticise but the winter cereals which had been sown provided a good deal of scope for scorn. Rough, rough. The ground was only half made in many fields and it was often hard to say whether the ground had been sown or whether it was just ploughed and turned green by volunteers.

We so wanted to find out for sure but it is awkward at the best of times. You are liable to get a thick ear if you ask a farmer if he has sown that field or if it is just weeds. But when you are in foreign foreign

country and don't speak the language it is nearly impossible.

However we did have a couple of days of an interpreter and from one peasant farmer we got the answer without asking. He had given up working for one of the giant co-operative farms to start on his own. He told us he just couldn't stand the waste any more.

As an example he told us about the incentives they had introduced at harvest time. Combine drivers were paid by the tonne. So half a dozen combines were set loose on a field and proceeded to race each other round and round trying to claim as much tonnage as possible. With such a regime riddles were never cleaned, warning lights were ignored and as much as twenty per-cent went over the tail of the combine.

As if that wasn't enough, the lorry drivers are also paid on tonnage. This means that the drivers load their carts too full and then do a Brands Hatch down to the store, shealing the grain out at every corner and every bump, in a desperate chase to jump the queue for the next load. "The result is our pigeons are very fat".

Having said all that, there

HE SAYS ... THE OTHER SIDE OF THE FIELD IS THAT WAY, BUT IT'S TOO FAR AWAY TO SEE!

Turnbull

INTERPRETER

OIST WAIT TILL I TELL THE 'GRAIN BARONS' ABOOT THIS!

were many farms, perhaps one in four, where they clearly know just what they were doing. We saw some of the finest seedbeds we've ever seen. Stoneless loams from light brown to "Howe o' the Mearns" red.

And what parks. Cairnadailly had nothing on these. It was unusual to be able to see the other side of any field even on a fine day. Each shift just seemed to go until it met the next road or a natural break, such as a river. It is said that the ploughmen, paid by the mile rather than the acre, just set out in the morning, plough straight till piece time and then turn to land back at the start in time for lunch. No time is consumed in turning.

What a splendid yoke for growing cereals. I could hardly wait for the discussion group to tell Mossie and the Red Rooster all about it. They may be grain Barons here but they would be crofters in Hungary.

I was quite elated when I approached the pub at the clay pigeon range where we have our Sunday night meetings. The car park was full. A suitable audience seemed to be in prospect for my traveller's tales.

177

Picture my disappointment then to find only Mossie and Crookie were there of the usual crowd. Not even a quorum. I asked the barman where all the car drivers were. It was Mossie who explained. "Business has been a bit slow and four of these cars are the landlord's. They're just there as decoys".

When the Hungarians get their marketing up to that sort of pitch they'll be hard for even Cairnadailly to match.

Phone is a real turn-off

I'M IN what my mother used to call an "ill taen" with the telephone. It's not the convenience of being able to reach half the world without leaving my house to which I object, but the fact that half the world can reach me. As I am out all day and my phone is unmanned, everyone is waiting for me when I get in. And the only thing I like to watch on the tele (apart from Scotland beating England at anything) is the news. But the sort of people who like to phone me have no interest in the news and at nine o'clock sharp they all reach for the phone. And they are not the worst. Far worse are those who phone me rather than watch *News at Ten*, by which time they often catch me in bed.

The failure to come to terms with the phone is not inherited. My late grandfather, Maitland Mackie of North Ythsie, was a master. For example, he was quick to see that all those twopenny calls could mount up and that, while all manner of things could be said to all manner of people on the phone, there was very little that couldn't wait... for a while at least.

That realisation he put to the saving of a great deal of money over the years. Instead of doing it the modern way and phoning everyone to whom he ever thought of saying anything, the old man used to make a careful note of all such trivia, and indeed of anything of a non-urgent nature. He knew that most of the people he wanted to speak to would eventually phone him. He'd be ready then. Out would come the diary and he'd get all his business done at the cost of nothing but a little patience.

That was to work particularly well in his dealings with his sons, who were put early into farms of their own. Old Maitland saw no need to have overheads in his business which could just as well be borne by the boys. They were forever phoning up for advice or to borrow this or that, and then their father would be ready with his diary.

In those days all calls had to go through the lady at the post office who had to speak to the lady in Aberdeen who then spoke to the post office lady in Auchterarder or wherever, so security was difficult. It wasn't unusual even thirty years ago to hear heavy breathing on the line during calls.

Well well, my grandfather, so it is said, had been discussing business on the telephone and the other party had asked a particularly delicate question concerning prices. "I don't think we should discuss that on the telephone,"said the old man, "They do say the lady at the post office sometimes listens in."

"I do not listen in," an angry voice interjected. "Fey on you Maitland Mackie for saying such a thing, and you an elder of the Kirk." Those were the days when being an elder of the kirk said a lot about a man's probity, or at least, about his care in not being found out.

She'd be damned if she'd let him away with that.

Of course the personal touch is gone from telephone exchanges. Even the lady at directory enquiries (who used to be so rude when you tried to tell her that the address you wanted to reach was a farm and therefore you couldn't give her the street name) disappears without a goodbye, and lets a machine tell you the number you require.

That trend was set by those infernal answering machines. Progress all seemed to happen at once for one of our neighbours here. Of my grandfather's generation, his bull had been ineffectual in settling one of his cows, and a friend had suggested he ring the AI.

Next week it was, "And did ye phone the AI?" "Oh aye, but I just got this wifie that kept newsin' awa' aboot my number and leavin' a message and widna' listen tae me so I just hung up and tried the bull again."

I really sympathise with that old man for I've never liked the answering machine. Usually it just means you've spent your money and haven't spoken to the person you wanted. I suppose if you're someone important like Margaret Thatcher or Benny Hill it may work, but I find that very few people ever ring me back.

And what about those Clever-Dicks who use the an-

swering device to riddle out the people they want to speak to from those they don't? If you have something they want you are half way through stammering out your message and feeling a right burke when they break in, and they have the cheek to be cheery about it, "Hallo Charlie, I'm here", they say as if they have made your day. They've been listening to you trying to talk to a machine and they used to put you away for trying that sort of thing.

I know old Maitland would have got a way to beat them. Perhaps he would have phoned when the machine was sure to be on, like the middle of the night, or when the football was on the tele. He might have left a message like this. "Aye Hilly, North Ythsie here. How are you and your good lady? If you have time please telephone me so that we can decide what to do about your good fortune. I think we should move quickly on this to make sure you get the maximum benefit and before Gurgedyke hears about it."

This would put Hilly into a frenzy of curiosity. He would call at once only to find that his good fortune was only to be offered some barley straw for sale and that Maitland Mackie had an extraordinarily long list of other things to discuss... at Hilly's expense.

November 5, 1990

A dear departed friend

THE MAIN event this week wasn't the gallant efforts of the lads from the National Farmer's Union of Scotland who went to Westminster to protect us all from "economic reality" but the funeral of an admirable neighbour. The tradition of honouring the neighbours as pall bearers was observed so I found myself in that role for the first time.

Now we in Buchan are not hard on our spiritual leaders. We don't expect them to lead us against the Moslems, or the Jews nor the Catholics. There isn't much opposition about. Even the Free Church has closed and the manse turned into a pub. We are likely wrong but, on the whole, we feel that we have got our direction and we don't need a high level of fervour from the minister.

But there is one thing we do expect. We get quite upset when, at a funeral, the minister says too much about the Almighty and not enough about

the deceased.

That could have been something of a dilemma at this week's funeral but the minister handled it beautifully. New to the parish, he really couldn't say a great deal about Sandy Taylor but he did a very good thing, we all thought. Having said what he could of our friend's life he then gave us a few minutes to think about what we remembered about this modest, remarkable man.

I had no difficulty with what to remember.

You see, fifty years ago Sandy Taylor was a horseman. Promoted from loon, too early and without training because so many of the older men were away to the war, he was cutting oats with the binder. As was the dangerous custom of the age, when the binder was choking, he would kick the straw to free it. He tried that once too often and by the time the horse stopped both his legs were mutilated.

182

The surgeons wanted to take them both off but the boy's mother would only let them take the worst one. She was right of course, and Sandy was left with one good leg and a wooden one. The way that he coped with that disability can still bring tears of admiration to my eyes.

With one leg he could no longer follow the plough so he took a job in the local garage. But that meant a walk of some three miles each way every day which would have been difficult if not impossible. He wouldn't be stuck though, and got a bike. He tied a cocoa tin to the peddle and put the peg leg into that to stop it slipping off.

Latterly he farmed the eight acres of the family croft in partnership with his big sister, and when the minister asked us at the funeral to remember Sandy in silence the image leapt up. He was sowing manure on his turnip ground, by hand out of a happer. It was clearly sore work for the wooden leg was a severe handicap in the ploughed ground. When he saw me he gave a cheery wave the warmth of which I shall not forget.

For me he epitomised then the spirit which turned the basically hostile environment of Buchan into the productive plain it now is.

Others will have had other images. There were still six brothers and sisters to remember the black house his parents moved to in 1911, and how their father had got the laird to come and see how badly a new house was needed. When Lord Aberdeen arrived he looked into the house, exclaimed "Good Lord!" and left to give the orders for a new house to be built.

Twelve children were raised in the new house and to this day the chiming clock (a wedding present made in Connecticut) is kept half an hour fast. That's because it took the gallant twelve just half an hour to get to school. That went in at nine o'clock so they had to leave at half past eight. "Whenever we heard the clock strike nine we were out of the door like a shot".

The last child left the school forty seven years ago but the clock is still kept half an hour in front.

As there were twelve of them the Taylor family have never been short of christenings, weddings, golden weddings and funerals to bring them together. But, in addition to those Christian rituals, the senior members maintained an older, pagan rite. They gathered each year at Ardo's hill to help Sandy with the leading.

Sandy drove his tractor between the stooks, a brother-in-law forked on the land, a neighbour built the carts, while one brother forked to the ruck, and another brother built the two stacks and the screw that the little field would yield. And the outside squad was inundated with sustenance provided by the sisters and sisters-in-law who followed the camp. The team, which last went into action in 1989, had an average age of well over seventy... so you can imagine it was a tidy job.

I'm proud to say that Sandy once asked me to build for him. And I'm sad to say that I had to decline. You see I had only once built a ruck and it was a middling success.

My father could see that the combined harvester was going to do away with all the old harvesting skills and determined that his son should build one ruck. The old grieve at Little Ardo supervised my building with no enthusiasm and a great deal of shaking of his head.

Despite a post being thrust into the side with the bulge in her my ruck had to be taken down the next day. It was in full view of the village too, but I have to say again my thanks to the grieve. He told them (when he was down for the papers) that I had lost my watch when building her and that we'd had to take the ruck right down to the found before we retrieved it.

That might have happened again had I agreed to help the Taylors with their harvest... and Sandy wouldn't have liked that.

Reps were not frank with us

IT WAS during a winter not very long ago when a young "representative" held a presentation designed to extol the virtues of his new cattle and sheep wormer to 150 farmers.

As has become more and more commonly the way in recent years, he had hired the function room in one of the pubs, laid on the stovie supper, the overhead projector and the video, and set out 180 chairs just in case. The bar would be open and the first drink would be free, and if there weren't too many people, he might stand the company's hand more often... and perhaps even often.

It was a dirty night, with a generous covering of snow, the wind offering to rise and the prospect of blocked roads. So, when half past seven came, only one farmer had turned up.

Half a dozen nervous jokes, and twenty minutes later, Mr. MacDonald of the Knapps was

still the whole audience.

150 platefuls of stovies not withstanding, the young salesman decided to call the meeting off and told his audience that he was sorry but it hardly seemed worth going through his presentation for one man, and in any case, with the way the wind was rising, maybe the farmer should be making his way home.

Mr. MacDonald replied thus; "Na, na laddie, that winna' dae. When I tak' a load o' hay up the hill to my ewes and only ane turns up, I dinna leave her hungry."

Properly chastened, the young man went ahead with the meeting. He found himself rather enjoying the situation, though he got little encouragement from Mr. MacDonald's demeanour. He sat there with his arms folded across his great chest and no expression at all on his face.

Still the show had to go on. When it came to questions Mr. MacDonald didn't have any so the salesman brought up the issues he had hoped would be asked, and when it came to the vote of thanks the rep. thanked the audience for it's kind attention.

"So how did you enjoy that, Mr. MacDonald", he asked?

"Over long."

"But Mr. MacDonald you told me about how when you only had one ewe you didn't deny her her meal and I've just treated you the same."

"That's as maybe laddie, but when I tak' a load o' hay up to my ewes and only ane appears I dinna gie' her the whole load."

I tell you that story because I found myself in a position similar to Mr. MacDonald this week.

It was an agro-chemical company which had taken one of the local boozers to promote a new type of sprayer. The impending meeting was the subject of much debate at the discussion group at which we were all bemoaning the latest round of rises in the price of liquid refreshment.

It was Mossie who saw the demonstration as a weapon in the fight against inflation. We would attend the presentation en masse, and drink our own healths at the company's expense. After all he and Crookie and the Red Rooster bought in excess of £100,000 worth of chemicals a year from the company so the least they could do was to sponsor an extra-curricular meeting of our discussion group.

It was agreed then. We would clear the decks, endure the presentation, have the jolliest of lunches and get the minibus to deliver us all home in time for our tea. The company could probably be conned into paying for that too as the last thing they would want was to get the blame for an entire discussion group losing it's licence.

It had been some time since I had kicked over the traces, so, with everything done or at least postponed, I set off with a gleam in my eye for the presentation.

What they were selling turned out to be a machine for spraying environmenticides onto the crops in a more economical way. Highly pressurised air was to be mixed with the chemicals and this would cut down the amount of the stuff that would drift onto your neighbours' crops and also reduce the amount that missed the crops and landed on the ground. The video and the young salesman (who also seemed to come out under pressure) assured us that scientific tests showed that, under that system, nearly half as much again of the environmenticide would land on the crop.

Then we had to go outside into the wind and the rain, for a demonstration which showed quite clearly that drift was reduced with the new machinery even if it was stiffer to buy. They then gave us a decent, if simple lunch of soup and ham sandwiches and drink if we wanted it.

"All very nice," you may think, but two things sickened me.

The first was that these people were ridiculously coy when we asked what savings there would be in chemicals if we bought the new equipment. It was at first denied that there would be any savings. It was just that more chemical would go on the plants and less on the ground and on neighbouring crops. Now I don't suppose there was anyone there (with the possible exception of the salesmen) who couldn't see that, if the plants were getting enough with the old system and they were now to get more chemical, then there was indeed scope for chemical savings.

We came to the conclusion that these people couldn't be frank with us because such an admission would be damaging to chemical sales. And I came to the conclusion that the discussion group were quite right not to take such commercial gatherings seriously but to use them as an opportunity for a cheap day out.

My second sickener was that, of the discussion group, I was the only one who turned up. By one-thirty I was back on the old cabless digger and composing a speech on my motion of "no confidence" to be put at next Sunday's meeting.

It's the obligation... not just the title deeds

FOR WEEKS now my farming has amounted to no more than waiting for the rain to stop. If only it would we could get the stones off the winter cereals and the rape, put on the sprays, batten down the hatches and wait for spring.

In the meantime, standing at the tractorshed door watching the rain cascading off the bothy roof has given me time to consider what it is that keeps me here. My wife's salary makes the profits of the farm look silly. I have had a real job that paid me a living wage in the town. So why don't I have a roup, sell the farm, invest the £400,000 at 10% and leave the land for a villa on the Costa-No-Vera-Much, or even for gainful employment?

Well, first of all, the farm isn't mine. The title deeds are in my name, of course, (jointly with my wife) but that is only the law of the land. There is an-

other law governing the ownership of Little Ardo. That law says the farm belongs to the family. Because I was an only child there was no one but me to take it on when my father was ready to leave "the cold shoulder of Scotland", as he called the North East.

I wouldn't like to give the impression that I was reluctant to take the farm. Far from it. I could think of no vocation that was more important. I was elated at the thought of gathering the stones that my great-great-grandfather overlooked. Of modernising the piggery my grandfather built and of adding profitability to the fertility my father fostered in Little Ardo's fields.

I couldn't claim to have been notably successful. My modernisation has included three sheds and about an acre of concrete but it still leaves me with the old steading which was falling down when my grandfather bought it from the laird in 1920. It is still falling down. The tractors were sixteen years old when I took over from my father and they are still eleven years old.

But profit was where I found it hard to match my ancestors. Even my father made a profit commensurate with his ambitions as a farmer. But buying my farm, stocking it and building my three new sheds soon meant that I was trying to make a thousand pounds a week just to pay the banker for his interest.

That's past me now, I'm very glad to say, and my overdraft is seasonal now, but getting to that position gave me (and Fiona) a pretty stiff row to hoe.

I wouldn't have it any other way, though. Only a peasant can understand how hurt I would have been to have let the farm decline or, worse and worse, go out of the family.

My grandfather, Maitland Mackie, used to take a handful of good loam and run it through his hands. Mind you, I think it was the love of good land anywhere that prompted that gesture. My father also used to take a handful of clean land, gaze at it in wonder and then rubbing his hands together, let it fall again to earth.

I don't think those men were really expressing a love of Little Ardo. After all they both got the place through their wives. I think Maitland Mackie's affair was with land in general and John Allan's with Aberdeenshire though there was also something sensuous for him in running the soil through his hands.

But for me it is Little Ardo. It has always been a special place for me. A place where I can feel in touch with nature and with my ancestors. As time goes on the feeling gets stronger. It becomes a religion.

There is a need in most of us to feel that the exertions of this world, with their triumphs and their tribulations, are not all there is. Religion and the concept of the Hereafter still fill that need for many. The true peasant who also has a religion is doubly blessed. For he has his land as his purpose and his God to fall back on.

But for me, though I have tried to believe in an organised God, there is only the land. With no God on whom to fall back the land becomes dearer and dearer as time devours my youth. It is all there is, outside my flesh and blood. It will endure.

So what, then, is Charlie Allan, peasant man, trying to do? Will he stay with his land until the black car climbs Ardo's hill to claim him. Till he goes to join the Yulls, the Mackies and the Allans now dead, in Methlick's old kirkyard?

I know an old man who has chosen that route to the graveyard. I saw him the other day. He's eighty-six now and needs two sticks since the replacement hips he got some time ago started to wear out. And yet he was pu'in' neeps with a tapner.

With the tapner under his arm and the two sticks working hard he made it to the drill. He then threw one stick and then the other a dozen yards or so down the drill and bent slowly to his task of cutting off the shaws and the roots.

When he reached the sticks he put the tapner down, used the sticks to give himself a stretch, threw them out in front of him again and picked up the tapner.

You can't but admire old Gordon Thomson. His is the spirit that carved Buchan from the moss. But it won't be my way.

Just as the waters of the Ythan which pass down through my land cannot be claimed. So the land should pass through me to another of the family. There is no need for me to die in harness. If I can just get it redd-up and the next generation to take it on, I'll be off.

I don't have to stay here to prove my love for the place. If I can pass it on to a follower who will accept the obligation as well as the title deeds, I can be like the Christian explorer who took his religion with him and roamed the world.

Digger saved by ellipse

IT IS a most riveting experience to turn round and see your digger trundling off. There are fields in Scotland where that would be no more than an inconvenience but not this one. The Piggery Park slopes gently enough at first, but not for long.

At the foot is what we call the Howe; the valley made by a stream which has long since gone underground. Forty years ago I used the steeps on the Howe for rolling Easter eggs, and twenty years ago I used to take my own children there to celebrate the rolling of the stone away from the door of the cave.

At a slope of one in something less than three, the Howe was also ideal for our attempts to ski. We had good balance and no fear but we could neither steer or stop. That didn't matter in the Howe. You went hurtling down the East side and came back to rest on the steep

Western bank.

As I watched the old digger accelerate towards the Howe on Friday my life flashed before my eyes. I remembered in 1946 sledging down it to join the cotter loons.

There had been a big blow the night before and a great ridge had formed from the top of the Howe. I couldn't see the danger and waved happily to the pals below.

They waved eagerly back and collapsed in happy laughter as I took off in the longest recorded flight on my sledge "Fleein' Flossy". I remember looking up at the great ridge of snow and seeing that I had fallen fifteen feet. Feet were smaller then so I guess it was only six, but I was badly shaken.

All this came to me as the old digger shuddered and shook down the Howe. I ran after her and saw her tear through the fence at the bottom of the Piggery. If there was to be another crash in the Howe I wanted to see it.

However, among the many idiosyncrasies of the Little Ardo digger is a very marked preference for turning right. When the power steering fluid is low the steering wheel has to be hauled to the left constantly.

And that flaw saved the old girl. Instead of hurtling straight down to her destruction she performed an ellipse and came to rest across the face of the brae. I was relieved, of course, but also a bit let down.

Now there were, in this neck of the woods, two meetings this week of relevance to the saga of the digger on auto-pilot.

The most important (and the most boring) was held by the Turriff branch of the National Farmer's Union. There Vice-President Maitland Mackie was explaining the marketing initiative he wants us all to join.

He wants to set up an inspectorate to ensure that we all adopt "Best Practices" and so earn "Farm Accreditation". This is a response to the demands being made by the supermarkets for food produced in conditions acceptable to their customers. They want to be able to assure the public that their food doesn't involve cruelty to animals, pollution of the environment, chemical residues and harm to wildlife.

The vision is of a Scottish farm industry having put it's own house in order while the rest of the European peasantry wait to have restrictions placed on them by governments.

Could we not then go to the government and tell them to keep out French Pâté as it is produced by forced-feeding of geese, all food from Eastern Europe because they haven't begun to think about the environment and all food from Spain until they stop the public torture of their bulls? At least we would be able to get on the side of the angels instead of resisting change all the time.

Of course, the arguments start when you consider just what should go in the scheme.

Well, the pig initiative is up and running fast. The buyers are responding in droves and by the tonne to such measures as the banning of sow tethers, mice in the feed stores and the casual use of antibiotics. To his initial chagrin Maitland Mackie's own farm at first failed to get accreditation, though he now sees that embarrassment as proof that the scheme is genuine.

It is clear that I will have to have my movement book and my medicines book in better-than-their-average shape and I suppose it can do us nothing but good to be a bit more efficient. If they stop us feeding mice and wasting chemicals the scheme will be part self-financing and anyway I'm sure it is a good way to go.

My other meeting was the annual dinner of the Ythanside Farmer's Club. The principal speaker was the delightful Patrick Gordon-Duff-Pennington. Apart from telling us (what we might have been able to guess) that he was fed up of having so many surnames, Patrick gave us the most pessimistic view of the future for our industry that I have ever heard in public.

The boss of the Scottish Landowners' Federation says we are in for six to eight years "hard labour" during which things will be as bad as ever they were in the 1890s or the 1930s. He says that if we don't borrow money we'll survive, but, if we are in debt, and there is still enough to buy ourselves a bungalow "then get out". If we can do without borrowing "do without the stuff".

So what am I to do?

Maitland Mackie will never say Little Ardo has 'Best Practice' as long as I have old machinery careering unmanned about the place. He will insist that I need a new digger. But Patrick won't let me borrow a penny to finance the deal.

It's a dilemma but at least I can sort that damned handbrake.

December 3, 1990

A bad week with the muckspreader

For the last three years or so the market for farms in the North East Corner has been dominated by what has come to be known, not always with affection, as "the white settlers". Since a farming weekly carried the headline "A County for Sale", something like nine tenths of farms which have come on the market have found buyers, not from the indigenous farming community, but from the South.

I was set to wondering what on earth makes them want to settle here. After all, they are not the prisoners of their family histories, as I am.

It was when I was spreading muck. Now, I don't believe even the most ardent organic farmer would see muckspreading as an encouraging way to spend a day of rain, even in ideal circumstances, and these circumstances were far from ideal.

Apart from the fact that the old digger only protects me

from water that comes straight down, the biggest trouble was a mistake that I had made all last winter and which my tenants had made when I was away in Africa for three years.

Laziness and a lack of familiarity with the big round bale had meant that my muck contained something in the region of a three per-cent admixture of baler twine, net and black polythene wrapper.

In case you are still spreading your muck with a graip let me explain that the modern spreader, consists of a cylinder in which a drive shaft rotates. Suspended from the shaft are a large number of chains with hammers on the ends. These chains are driven frantically round and that throws the muck out over the field... in theory.

But the theory breaks down if you have foreign bodies in the muck.

The first load revealed the problem. Only about half of it came out of the spreader be-

195

cause the chains had got completely snarled up. The hammers had become wrapped tightly round the chain and could not get hold of the anything to throw.

There was nothing for it but to get into the spreader with a graip, a sharp knife and the patience of Job.

Each load took nearer to an hour than the ten minutes it should have taken. I could see myself spending all winter spreading this muck or perhaps even dying in the attempt.

However at the weekend Potions (the local chemist) came to play and we developed a system which, though no better fun, at least started the stuff moving. While he was away spreading each load I would shake out the next lot with the digger and remove the worst of the wrapping. When he returned each time we would both fall to and clean out what I had missed in the previous load.

We got up to a fill every fifteen minutes that way, but it was while I was sifting that I had my accident.

I was turning to put an armful of soggy twine and netting on the heap when my left wellington came off... sock and all. There I was in a ten inches of slurry with one foot in the air.

It is some time since I was an athlete but I still have pretty good balance and managed to hop through the slurry to the missing wellie. From it I managed to retrieve the sock. But my troubles had only started. I found it very difficult to get the sock on again and let my bare foot somewhat into the muck. I could hardly put the sock onto such a filthy foot so my next few minutes were spent trying to wipe it on the back of my standing leg... the arthritic nature of which was being emphasised by the minute.

To cut a long story short I finally made a desperate lunge to get the sock on and succeeded, but only at the expense of loosing my balance altogether and plunging the bootless foot deep into the slurry, sock and all.

It was cold as well as humiliating and it was then, as I sloshed my way out of the midden, that I thought of the white settlers and why they would choose to be farmers here when they weren't born to it.

Of course there are settlers of all sorts. There is the plumber who suddenly found that with the inflation of property values, his buildings where he conducted a profitless business were worth over three hundred thousand and thought that would last a long time in farming. He and the goodlifers must be beginning to see that there isn't much fun in standing on one leg, trying to get your sock back on in a foot of slurry.

But I did get chapter and verse from one white settler this week. He came to farm in the North East for what look like good reasons and, in his third year says he wouldn't have it otherwise.

Hal Junker had always wanted to be a farmer and had worked hard with his wife to that end. Saving hard from a job with the Mole Valley Co-op they had worked their ways up to a sixty-six acre farm in Devon when he got the chance to buy in Scotland. They were able to buy three hundred and fifty better acres and still have something left with which to stock the bigger unit.

And Mr. Junker is happy here. He says it is much healthier for the livestock here, the ground doesn't poach like the fields in Devon, and the fields are bigger, flatter and are much more suitable for cereals.

Makes you wonder who wanted that pretty useless unit in Devon so badly that he would pay enough to buy the sort of unit so many young Scottish farmers dream of. The answer of course is that it wasn't farmer demand that created that market.

The price of land in Devon is determined by the housing boom created by the yuppies.

It seems a sad reflection on our great industry that the price of farms should have so little to do with their ability to produce food and so much to do with location.

December 10, 1990

Amiable army on the move

I'VE BEEN reflecting, without rancour, on the increasing army of white-collar-and-black-shoe workers who are appearing on my farm.

We had one this week; an amiable ex-policeman who has got the job of touring Aberdeenshire to inspect farmer's livestock movement books, to ensure that we have ear tags in all our calves, and that we have a herd book which relates each cow to each tagged calf.

Luckily it was a miserable day and we didn't have to go out to inspect the calves ears. And the new herd-books which, since November 15, it has been compulsory to keep, aren't out yet so all we had to go over was the movement book.

I have to admit mine is an unimpressive document, but I was let off with a warning that from now on the administration of cattle had to be by the book and that the rules were to be enforced. That was a bit of a disappointment, I can tell you,

as it was my first visit on that business in seventeen years... now I can look forward to six monthly grillings.

How things have changed. When I took over at Little Ardo 17 years ago I also took over the great Jimmy Low who was at that time a veteran of some forty summers in the place. I had grand ideas about pedigree breeding and would start a card index for all the livestock. Jimmy would have nothing to do with it.

"Na, na. I've managed for forty year withoot writin' onything doon and I'm nae gaun tae start noo. If ye canna mind what you've been deein' ye shouldna be deein' it".

Well, that was all very well as long as Jimmy was about for he did remember everything he had done. And anyway, everything was more relaxed then. He told me that when my grandfather was applying for a licence to produce milk here, the grieve told the "sanitary"

198

thirty-six lies. And they wouldn't have expected it any other way fifty years ago.

Old Jimmy never had a licence for the ancient shotgun that he kept behind the door and neither did he have a locking cupboard in which to keep it and its ammunition.

I've seen to that at last but there is so much more of that sort of thing to do before I can sleep easy.

Take safety. The man from the Health and Safety Executive can close you down if the farm isn't safe and everybody tells me that there is a big push on and the "Safety" will be round any day now.

Well, I can't really complain about that as there is only me here to protect and I need all the protection I can get.

To tell the truth I am not at all clear what I have to do to make the place safe though I have done somethings to clean up my act. After twelve years I have finally got a safety guard for the bruiser, though it's not on yet, I've got a locking store for the chemicals that used to lie about wherever the lorry dropped them, and I've bought from the department (at great expense) the poster which it is necessary to display warning of dangers to my staff.

I am absolutely confident that when the Safety man does come he'll be able to help me with other suggestions.

Of course he may have difficulty in getting in about to the place, so numerous are my official visitors.

I've had the man that counts the cows to make sure that I'm not claiming too many beef cow premia or too many hill cow subsidies. I had enough cows all right but using the sort of skill a man like that has he was able to point out to me that I had one heifer which, according to my records, had not calved. It had not died, it had not been sold and yet it was no longer on the place.

Not being an accomplished liar like Old Jimmy and lacking his memory I had to admit that I knew not.

If that was embarrassing it wasn't half so bad as when the Variable Premium man came.

He was making sure that I hadn't been claiming on cattle which weren't mine and it took my somewhat casual farm accounts two visits to disgorge all the evidence that was required to satisfy the V.P. man.

Then there was the Vatman. He turned out to be a delightful chap who took the job to get a little bit of excitement into his life. Prison officer in the Maze in Northern Ireland just hadn't had enough pace for him.

Anyway he was far too fast for me. The visit cost me some four hundred pounds. I have discovered that many of my fellow farmers are making the same mistakes as I was so I'll tell you. It could save you a red face.

The party to which I invite all those who help to keep the rocky ship Ardo afloat may or may not be allowable for tax purposes as an expense of the business, but I was quite wrong to re-claim the vat. Then there was the petrol. I get an account from the garage which includes repairs and petrol. I claimed the lot but should have left the petrol out as it's dealt with separately.

I know I'm not finished yet either. In the old days we used to leave the antibiotic bottle handy for the calves pen where it might be needed at any time for scours or it would be down by the cattle crush to catch a foul of the foot.

But that won't do now. We've got to have a child-proof case and a book into which we write every dose we give with details of which beast got it and where the drugs came from. I'm so daunted by that idea that I now let the vets do it all though I do have the safe cupboard and the book.

I don't even know who it is that comes to inspect that side but I'm sure he's on his way.

A new grieve for Mossside

I'VE TOLD you often that, whereas my father farmed Little Ardo with a staff of six, I have to struggle on alone. Well, it would be about a year ago that I was discussing our generation's much reduced circumstances with the farmer of Mossside. And despite the fact that Mossie's circumstances are not nearly as reduced as my own, he was agreeing with me and shaking his head in a way usually reserved for much older men.

It was indeed damnable but whereas I saw our misfortune as my not having enough money to pay a man, he thought there just wasn't sufficient qualified manpower available to give him the life of ease to which he aspired and which both our fathers had claimed as a right.

It was after a considerable session of this head-shaking, pregnant pausing and sighing for the good old days that Mossie declared "There's only one thing for it. We'll just hae tae breed wir own."

That solution was out of the question for me with this country's monogamous ways so I thought no more about it. But Mossie wasn't joking. I am writing this through the hangover generated in the interests of wetting the head of the next grieve of Mossside.

I have to say that, at the time and in the places that I did my breeding, the chore of wetting the babies head was no more than a question of toasting the new arrival at the first occasion when strong drink was taken. In the normal course of events that never involved undue delay but there was never any question of a special event.

It seems that now a new and dangerous tradition is developing. It is a new bastion of male chauvinism at which all those wrecks who used to be "the lads" foregather to explore the limits of human tolerance to alcohol, protein and sleep deprivation.

We'd been warned so the loins were well girded when the call came. "Aye Charlie, the wife's awa' tae the hospital, the pigs awa' tae the killin' hoose and the party's at the Salmon Inn at four o'clock on Sunday."

Hardly surprisingly after a break of eleven years, Mossie had had to make considerable concessions to get his scheme off the ground. He has had to agree to take considerably more interest in the new arrival than he ever showed previously. It was made quite clear that there was no question of the old pram being made to do.

And that was a sore point. The new pram cost more than the pickup truck on which Mossie and his two brothers learned to terrorise the farm not twenty years ago. "That's inflation for you and it hasna' even got an engine".

Worse than that, the price doesn't even include the extras like the dual wheels he's had fitted so he can combine the long pram pushing walks he's promised with his constant monitoring of the cereal crops.

Despite those fearsome and unbudgeted-for overheads no on-cost was to be spared and a whole pig was to be spit-roasted for the head-wetting.

Of course, that method of cooking pork hasn't been much in vogue around here for the last five hundred years, so there weren't many spits available. Resourceful as ever the hero adapted the rotaspreader as a gas-fired rotisserie. This wasn't an immediate success as the power-take-off of the tractor was so fast that it took ages to heat up. And when it did eventually start to sizzle the fat of the pig was, sprayed round the Salmon in a way which was a fire hazard and bad for the guests best clothes.

As I live but a few miles from the Salmon Inn, and as I suspected there might be some fairly competitive drinking, I decided to take the bike. It was during the cold snap last week and I found that I had the greatest difficulty remaining in the saddle and in fact fell off twice to the discomfort of my arthritic knees.

On the way I passed the old joiner's shop where a hundred years ago the great Geordie Paterson hosted a memorable stag night. That one had been the picturesque ceremony in which, in preparation for coming in a fit state to his bride the young man had his feet washed by his friends. But even then the tradition had degenerated into a drunken brawl at which the last thing that was washed was the groom's feet.

Geordie, the millwright, was for none of that sort of horseplay and escaped by fiendish cunning.

He agreed to the feet-washing and invited all the young roughs of the area to a grand do in the joiner's shop. He provided four gallons of whisky. He hosted an excellent party and when he had them all threequarters drunk he locked them all in with enough of the whisky left to finish the job.

By the time the sore heads arose the wedding was on and the bird had flown.

Mossie's do wasn't as bad as that. I arrived on my bike to a suitable cheer at the back of four and left at two the next morning considerably the better of drink. And if you doubt that I was the better of the drink I have proof positive; I sped home on my trusty bike as though I was still a young loon going home from school.

I don't suppose the baby will be any the better for our efforts but certainly Mossie seemed very happy with Jill's arrival... it's high time there was a lady grieve in Aberdeenshire.

December 24, 1990

Suntie appears on the roof

IF YOU'RE not distracted by the festivities you'll be reading this on Christmas Eve. I need no more excuse to tell you of the great Christmas fantasy created by an uncle of mine in the late nineteen forties.

Those were the days before you had to get up extra early to to get the beasts done, in time to get the turkey on and the Santa suit on, then welcome the revellers who had come to see if you'd made a right job of wrapping the stuff you'd spent all week buying for them.

I don't mean that those things weren't done, only that I wasn't doing them. That was the lot of the adults. And the adults among the farmers of the two to four pair places of Aberdeenshire didn't have to do all of it themselves in those days. They had men to feed the beasts and many still had help in the house.

It was those staff who made it possible for the children in my family to enjoy the most delicious fantasy that Christmas. Walt Disney would have been proud of it.

We were at a party at Westertown of Rothienorman, which was at that time farmed by the Maitland Mackie who was chairman of the Aberdeen and District Marketing Board for so long.

We all knew there would be a Santa and that he would have some rather boring present for each of us, but we couldn't have dreamed of the lengths to which the old folks would go to thrill us.

Suddenly the chairman of the milk board said; "Shush everyone. Can you hear anything?" We all listened and, sure enough, somewhere outside, there was a shrilling of sleigh bells. We all rushed out.

There on the lawn was a searchlight which had been liberated from the Oldmeldrum Home Guard. With that the chairman of the milk board scoured the skies while a voice

204

which grew evermore impatient kept shouting from the heavens, "Na, na. Ower here."

I knew almost at once that the voice was coming from the roof, but for some reason the chairman kept sweeping the skies till the sixty children were all screaming at him to light up the roof of the old farmhouse.

and on.

After a considerable debate as to which chimney he should come down, Santa mounted the sleigh and, with much creaking of pulleys, the contraption shoogled across the roof to the side where we had all told him the sitting room chimney was to be found.

Turnbull.

Eventually he gave in and swept the light round. There on the roof was Santa, complete with sleigh and cardboard reindeer.

"Is this Westertown?" roared the jolly red giant.

"Yes." we all chimed back.

"Is Maitland Mackie here?"

"Yes."

"Is Charlie Allan here?"

"Yes." And so on and on

When he put his first foot inside the lum the searchlight went out and we all rushed in to greet him and get our presents.

But he wasn't there.

At last muffled and realistic cries of claustrophobic terror were heard from a bedroom above and we all rushed there. We could see that there had been considerable masonery activity in the room recently for a new fireplace seemed to have been put in. There dangling down from the chimney was Santa's size twelve wellie.

We tried to pull him down but he was quite stuck. As many as could get hold of a wellie grabbed and pulled just like calving a Friesian heifer, but, just like a Friesian heifer, the lum was too ungenerously structured.

Eventually tools were sent for, and the brand new fireplace was torn down, I remember thinking that it was lucky that the cement was still wet.

It was a magic occasion and not at all spoiled by the fact that I thought the giant wellie looked so like our grandfather's. He was visibly shaken and it was some little time before he was able to give us our presents.

Happy Christmas.